SO-AWI-268

WORDLY WISE 3000® THIRD EDITION

BOOK 11

Test Booklet

Systematic Academic Vocabulary Development

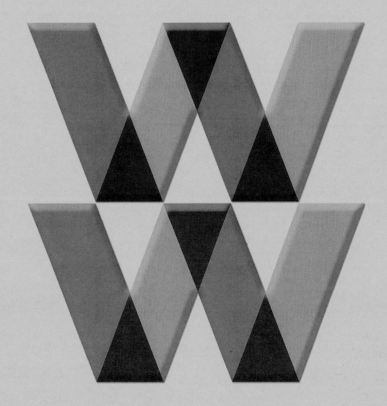

School Specialty, Inc.
Cambridge and Toronto

© 2012 by School Specialty, Inc. All rights reserved. No part of this book may be reproduced or utilized in any form or by any electronic or mechanical means, including photocopying, without permission in writing from the publisher.

Printed in Hudson, NH, in November 2018
ISBN 978-0-8388-7667-1

5 6 7 8 KSP 21 20 19 18

Name _____   Date _____

Find a SYNONYM for each bold word. Then fill in the circle next to your answer.

1. Although she is a novice, Rena **exudes** confidence in her abilities.

   Ⓐ disguises
   Ⓑ lacks
   Ⓒ exhibits
   Ⓓ suppresses

2. The president **convened** a cabinet meeting.

   Ⓐ summoned
   Ⓑ forgot
   Ⓒ dismissed
   Ⓓ remembered

3. Most urban legends are based on **apocryphal** stories.

   Ⓐ accurate
   Ⓑ spurious
   Ⓒ historical
   Ⓓ authentic

4. The river circled the **periphery** of the city.

   Ⓐ suburbs
   Ⓑ center
   Ⓒ edge
   Ⓓ harbor

5. The scale's needle **vacillated** between four and five grams before finally settling between the two.

   Ⓐ tended
   Ⓑ balanced
   Ⓒ wavered
   Ⓓ struggled

Find an ANTONYM for each bold word. Then fill in the circle next to your answer.

6. Paul was a valued party guest because of his skill as a **raconteur.**

   Ⓐ clown
   Ⓑ bore
   Ⓒ comic
   Ⓓ friend

7. Laura used **subterfuge** to escape punishment for cutting class.

   Ⓐ lies
   Ⓑ enemies
   Ⓒ skill
   Ⓓ honesty

© SSI • DO NOT DUPLICATE

8. Lorenzo was **mortified** by his fall in the lunchroom.

   Ⓐ pleased
   Ⓑ angered
   Ⓒ injured
   Ⓓ shamed

9. Yolanda's habit of studying with **expedient** memory devices, rather than taking the time to truly learn the material, proved a failure in the end.

   Ⓐ speedy
   Ⓑ inconvenient
   Ⓒ direct
   Ⓓ impersonal

10. High-level mathematics can be **arcane** to the layperson.

    Ⓐ mysterious
    Ⓑ useful
    Ⓒ unimportant
    Ⓓ simple

Choose the best way to complete each sentence or answer each question. Then fill in the circle next to your answer.

11. Which of the following would you most likely use to **gesticulate?**

    Ⓐ a lantern
    Ⓑ your hands
    Ⓒ flowers
    Ⓓ a pencil

12. **Incremental** change happens

    Ⓐ in huge leaps.
    Ⓑ a little at a time.
    Ⓒ in unknown amounts.
    Ⓓ without outside help.

13. In which of the following situations are you likely to find **levity?**

    Ⓐ at a funeral
    Ⓑ during a final exam
    Ⓒ at a party
    Ⓓ standing in a long line

14. Which of the following is most likely to be described as **imperturbable?**

    Ⓐ a rodeo bull
    Ⓑ a killer bee
    Ⓒ a wild bear
    Ⓓ a guide dog

15. **Peripheral** vision relates to things you can see

    Ⓐ to the side.
    Ⓑ straight ahead.
    Ⓒ in the dark.
    Ⓓ moving quickly.

© SSI • DO NOT DUPLICATE

Standardized Test Preview/Practice

1. VACILLATE : DECIDE ::

   Ⓐ procrastinate : act

   Ⓑ embarrass : brag

   Ⓒ despair : attempt

   Ⓓ withdraw : hide

   Ⓔ excite : enjoy

2. RACONTEUR : STORY ::

   Ⓐ cook : dining

   Ⓑ magician : rabbit

   Ⓒ virtuoso : music

   Ⓓ office : law

   Ⓔ librarian : books

3. It had been two weeks since Britney's head cold first appeared, and she was now — for an expedient to — her symptoms.

   Ⓐ waiting . . moderate

   Ⓑ hesitant . . mask

   Ⓒ doubtful . . improve

   Ⓓ desperate . . alleviate

   Ⓔ eager . . worsen

4. Maple trees exude —, which can be boiled into — and served with waffles.

   Ⓐ leaves . . jelly

   Ⓑ sap . . syrup

   Ⓒ aromas . . seasonings

   Ⓓ bark . . paste

   Ⓔ roots . . porridge

5. As if reiterating the — about seatbelts a dozen times a day were not enough, his mother — the same gesticulation representing fastening a seatbelt every time Paolo left the house.

   Ⓐ threat . . brandished

   Ⓑ rule . . played

   Ⓒ warning . . indicated

   Ⓓ promise . . shouted

   Ⓔ reminder . . performed

© SSI • DO NOT DUPLICATE

Lesson 2 Test

Find a SYNONYM for each bold word. Then fill in the circle next to your answer.

1. Owning a vintage limited edition Rolls Royce is a display of great **opulence.**

   Ⓐ intelligence
   Ⓑ skill
   Ⓒ wealth
   Ⓓ rudeness

2. Reid was **disconcerted** by the stranger's barrage of personal questions.

   Ⓐ charmed
   Ⓑ flustered
   Ⓒ enlightened
   Ⓓ pleased

3. Some sports fans can get **choleric** when they think a referee makes a bad call.

   Ⓐ giddy
   Ⓑ self-righteous
   Ⓒ disappointed
   Ⓓ angry

4. The police are seeking a **marauder** whose reputation has made people all over Connecticut feel unsafe in their homes.

   Ⓐ thief
   Ⓑ shoplifter
   Ⓒ racketeer
   Ⓓ embezzler

5. Fresh air and sunshine can have a **therapeutic** effect on people.

   Ⓐ sickening
   Ⓑ healthful
   Ⓒ terrifying
   Ⓓ depressing

Find an ANTONYM for each bold word. Then fill in the circle next to your answer.

6. Grandmother wished she had a more **utilitarian** design.

   Ⓐ awkward
   Ⓑ impractical
   Ⓒ realistic
   Ⓓ overbearing

7. Melinda's clients valued her **patrician** style of interior design.

   Ⓐ unrefined
   Ⓑ elegant
   Ⓒ stingy
   Ⓓ inherited

© SSI • DO NOT DUPLICATE

8. Her father knew Lina was sick when she remained **phlegmatic** even when he offered to take her out for a pancake breakfast.

    Ⓐ calm
    Ⓑ excited
    Ⓒ belligerent
    Ⓓ practical

9. Sonya's **choleric** brother was always unpredictable in public.

    Ⓐ funny
    Ⓑ excitable
    Ⓒ calm
    Ⓓ nervous

10. As soon as they started hitting below the belt, the referee **interposed** himself between the boxers.

    Ⓐ intervened
    Ⓑ removed
    Ⓒ relaxed
    Ⓓ positioned

Choose the best way to complete each sentence or answer each question. Then fill in the circle next to your answer.

11. Which of the following would be considered **accoutrements** of a painter?

    Ⓐ museums
    Ⓑ lenses
    Ⓒ brushes
    Ⓓ visitors

12. Which of the following is most likely to be among Africa's **fauna?**

    Ⓐ an oasis
    Ⓑ a rhinoceros
    Ⓒ a palm tree
    Ⓓ a violet

13. Someone with a **propensity** for fighting has

    Ⓐ a largely peaceful personality.
    Ⓑ an ability to win most fights.
    Ⓒ a belief that fighting is wrong.
    Ⓓ a tendency to get into fights.

14. A gymnast with only a **modicum** of grace is likely to give what type of performance?

    Ⓐ a clumsy one
    Ⓑ a stellar one
    Ⓒ an agile one
    Ⓓ an expert one

15. Drew could only feel **aggrieved** when the scholarship committee treated him so

    Ⓐ kindly.
    Ⓑ generously.
    Ⓒ enthusiastically.
    Ⓓ unfairly.

© SSI • DO NOT DUPLICATE

Standardized Test Preview/Practice

1. UTILITARIAN : DECADENT ::

    Ⓐ patrician : wealthy

    Ⓑ apocryphal : odd

    Ⓒ frivolous : serious

    Ⓓ needy : charitable

    Ⓔ ornate : expensive

2. MARAUD : PIRATE ::

    Ⓐ cook : chef

    Ⓑ camouflage : hunter

    Ⓒ rehearse : dancer

    Ⓓ laugh : children

    Ⓔ recover : nurse

3. Because of Alan's reputation for being choleric, Cheryl — to invite him to her party. But he comported himself so —, she did not regret her decision to include him.

    Ⓐ dreaded . . obnoxiously

    Ⓑ was thrilled . . aggressively

    Ⓒ was afraid . . rudely

    Ⓓ hesitated . . pleasantly

    Ⓔ rushed . . politely

4. Stefan's story of an encounter with an alligator in Idaho does not comport with my — of the — fauna.

    Ⓐ fears . . reptilian

    Ⓑ nightmares . . monstrous

    Ⓒ understanding . . regional

    Ⓓ suspicions . . seasonal

    Ⓔ theories . . carnivorous

5. Though not of — parents, Kendra fancies herself a patrician since her great-aunt married a duke.

    Ⓐ immigrant

    Ⓑ important

    Ⓒ foreign

    Ⓓ rich

    Ⓔ noble

© SSI • DO NOT DUPLICATE

Lesson 3 Test

Find a SYNONYM for each bold word. Then fill in the circle next to your answer.

1. The class could feel the **vibrant** percussions of the drum corps rehearsing downstairs.

   Ⓐ vibrating
   Ⓑ pounding
   Ⓒ relentless
   Ⓓ distracting

2. Ashley was reluctant to admit it, but doing all the required reading for an assignment was an **efficacious** way to prepare for the test.

   Ⓐ easy
   Ⓑ speedy
   Ⓒ effective
   Ⓓ entertaining

3. The losing team seemed **stoic** in the face of defeat.

   Ⓐ reluctant
   Ⓑ devastated
   Ⓒ pathetic
   Ⓓ indifferent

4. Army training **inculcates** soldiers with values of teamwork and discipline.

   Ⓐ teaches
   Ⓑ rewards
   Ⓒ alienates
   Ⓓ requires

5. The painter's **stellar** representations of light in different seasons and at different times of day impressed even the normally jaded critics.

   Ⓐ unique
   Ⓑ ordinary
   Ⓒ outlandish
   Ⓓ outstanding

Find an ANTONYM for each bold word. Then fill in the circle next to your answer.

6. Gymnasts perform **prodigious** acts of flexibility and strength.

   Ⓐ repeated
   Ⓑ ordinary
   Ⓒ skillful
   Ⓓ wondrous

7. Ever since he received the telescope for his birthday, Travis has been preoccupied with **stellar** occurrences.

   Ⓐ arcane
   Ⓑ earthly
   Ⓒ repeated
   Ⓓ boring

© SSI • DO NOT DUPLICATE

8. Keri decorated her room with the **vibrant** colors that streaked the sky at sunset.

  Ⓐ mixed
  Ⓑ bright
  Ⓒ dull
  Ⓓ primary

9. The **efficacy** of many prescription drugs depends on the patient's proper usage.

  Ⓐ value
  Ⓑ content
  Ⓒ failure
  Ⓓ power

10. Dani's refusal to think, read, or write will cause her mind to **atrophy.**

  Ⓐ develop
  Ⓑ waste
  Ⓒ remember
  Ⓓ succeed

Choose the best way to complete each sentence or answer each question. Then fill in the circle next to your answer.

11. You are most likely to receive an **emolument** when you

  Ⓐ commit a crime.
  Ⓑ find change on the sidewalk.
  Ⓒ finish a week of work.
  Ⓓ need to be vaccinated.

12. Stanley prepared for the marathon with a daily workout **regimen. A regimen** is

  Ⓐ a strategy.
  Ⓑ a philosophy.
  Ⓒ an obsession.
  Ⓓ a routine.

13. Because of his refusal to bend any rule, Coach Brown was known to be a **martinet.** He is most likely

  Ⓐ strict.
  Ⓑ well-loved.
  Ⓒ a performer.
  Ⓓ successful.

14. While everyone else was hysterical, Lance, always the **stoic,** seemed

  Ⓐ jovial.
  Ⓑ unaffected.
  Ⓒ angry.
  Ⓓ spiritual.

15. If a painting is described as an **icon,** it is likely to be

  Ⓐ popular.
  Ⓑ religious.
  Ⓒ controversial.
  Ⓓ disturbing.

© SSI • DO NOT DUPLICATE

Standardized Test Preview/Practice

1. ICON : IDOLIZED ::

   Ⓐ clown : amused

   Ⓑ waiter : respected

   Ⓒ monster : feared

   Ⓓ politician : despised

   Ⓔ hero : mocked

2. INESTIMABLE : MEASURED ::

   Ⓐ forgettable : described

   Ⓑ apparent : decided

   Ⓒ frequent : listed

   Ⓓ infinite : counted

   Ⓔ loud : heard

3. The symbol was — as an icon for the fast food chain.

   Ⓐ confused

   Ⓑ recognized

   Ⓒ worshiped

   Ⓓ idolized

   Ⓔ mistaken

4. Without his wildly zealous — in attendance, the comedian's — was more lackluster.

   Ⓐ critics . . audience

   Ⓑ peers . . ego

   Ⓒ fans . . performance

   Ⓓ rivals . . confidence

   Ⓔ family . . wardrobe

5. As the prodigious — of the circus animals moved through our town, the streets were vibrant with — of jungles, savannahs, and forests.

   Ⓐ parade . . sounds

   Ⓑ size . . colors

   Ⓒ weight . . memories

   Ⓓ speed . . textures

   Ⓔ operators . . tastes

© SSI • DO NOT DUPLICATE

Lesson 4 ▷ Test

Find a SYNONYM for each bold word. Then fill in the circle next to your answer.

1. Viking marauders **pillaged** villages along the Atlantic coast.

   Ⓐ inhabited
   Ⓑ built
   Ⓒ abandoned
   Ⓓ plundered

2. Many fugitives try to travel **incognito.**

   Ⓐ alone
   Ⓑ together
   Ⓒ unrecognized
   Ⓓ frequently

3. Mark would not give up his **hapless** attempts at a writing career despite repeated failure.

   Ⓐ addictive
   Ⓑ unfortunate
   Ⓒ successful
   Ⓓ repeated

4. Premeditated murder is among the most **heinous** of crimes.

   Ⓐ illegal
   Ⓑ regrettable
   Ⓒ savage
   Ⓓ evil

5. Gross anatomy, a class taken in the first year of medical school, **indoctrinates** some students and convinces others to pursue a different career.

   Ⓐ trains
   Ⓑ changes
   Ⓒ graduates
   Ⓓ needs

Find an ANTONYM for each bold word. Then fill in the circle next to your answer.

6. The uninitiated should be **circumspect** about mountain biking.

   Ⓐ excited
   Ⓑ reckless
   Ⓒ careful
   Ⓓ fearful

7. Running for political office requires great **composure** under the constant attacks from opponents and scrutiny from the media.

   Ⓐ money
   Ⓑ calm
   Ⓒ agitation
   Ⓓ thievery

© SSI • DO NOT DUPLICATE

8. Ms. Diaz was appointed **interim** principal after Mr. Gresham's sudden departure.

   Ⓐ substitute
   Ⓑ permanent
   Ⓒ emergency
   Ⓓ temporary

9. By donning a blonde wig and dark glasses, Bridget was able to walk **incognito** through her neighborhood.

   Ⓐ disguised
   Ⓑ recognized
   Ⓒ quietly
   Ⓓ well-dressed

10. Religious cults provide more **indoctrination** than spiritual guidance.

    Ⓐ training
    Ⓑ commercials
    Ⓒ objectivity
    Ⓓ humor

Choose the best way to complete each sentence or answer each question. Then fill in the circle next to your answer.

11. Which of the following is most likely to be found in the **environs** of a major city?

    Ⓐ a neighboring state
    Ⓑ suburbs
    Ⓒ rural areas
    Ⓓ countries

12. Where is a robin's egg most likely to be **ensconced?**

    Ⓐ in a nest
    Ⓑ on a shelf
    Ⓒ in a cupboard
    Ⓓ in a pantry

13. Lost in a **reverie** about her upcoming vacation, when the teacher called on her, Annie was

    Ⓐ frightened.
    Ⓑ thrilled.
    Ⓒ unprepared.
    Ⓓ ready.

14. Which is most likely to build an **edifice?**

    Ⓐ a science class
    Ⓑ a bird in a tree
    Ⓒ a child on a beach
    Ⓓ generations of researchers

15. Carson craved being **autonomous** at work so he could be

    Ⓐ supervised.
    Ⓑ independent.
    Ⓒ realistic.
    Ⓓ important.

© SSI • DO NOT DUPLICATE

Standardized Test Preview/Practice

1. MAUSOLEUM : TOMB ::

   Ⓐ limousine : chauffeur

   Ⓑ mansion : house

   Ⓒ tree : shrub

   Ⓓ office : penthouse

   Ⓔ gown : tuxedo

2. After his — on the mountain, Lloyd is more circumspect about future trips.

   Ⓐ experience

   Ⓑ enlightenment

   Ⓒ afternoon

   Ⓓ success

   Ⓔ accident

3. At least once a day, Daniel finds himself in a reverie where he has —.

   Ⓐ chores to do

   Ⓑ supernatural powers

   Ⓒ forgotten an assignment

   Ⓓ overslept

   Ⓔ soup for lunch

4. The interim — enjoyed her office atop the downtown edifice, even though she knew it was —.

   Ⓐ secretary . . dishonest

   Ⓑ intern . . rotating

   Ⓒ auditor . . permanent

   Ⓓ director . . temporary

   Ⓔ janitor . . accidental

5. HAPLESS : LUCK ::

   Ⓐ father : children

   Ⓑ rich : debt

   Ⓒ writer : imagination

   Ⓓ dancer : rhythm

   Ⓔ bald : hair

© SSI • DO NOT DUPLICATE

Lesson 5 Test

Find a SYNONYM for each bold word. Then fill in the circle next to your answer.

1. Her complicated teaching method makes simple subjects **abstruse.**

   Ⓐ easier
   Ⓑ intense
   Ⓒ difficult
   Ⓓ boring

2. If the club doubted Toby's **penitence** after he missed the fundraiser, his hard work at every subsequent event convinced them.

   Ⓐ regret
   Ⓑ embarrassment
   Ⓒ anger
   Ⓓ pride

3. The squad knew that practice was the key to winning, so their **acquiescence** to the intense rehearsal schedule came without a murmur of objection.

   Ⓐ support
   Ⓑ dissent
   Ⓒ acceptance
   Ⓓ commitment

4. The car salesperson's customers appreciated his **probity.**

   Ⓐ curiosity
   Ⓑ honesty
   Ⓒ fitness
   Ⓓ intelligence

5. After a heated debate, the manager **acquiesced** to Vance's demand for a raise.

   Ⓐ left
   Ⓑ complied
   Ⓒ disagreed
   Ⓓ shouted

Find an ANTONYM for each bold word. Then fill in the circle next to your answer.

6. The **surfeit** of ice cream varieties at the Dream Cream Ice Cream Parlor made it hard for Luz to decide which one she wanted in her sundae.

   Ⓐ abundance
   Ⓑ disrepair
   Ⓒ scarcity
   Ⓓ collection

7. Judging from that gory movie he took me to, Brian has **unsavory** tastes in film.

   Ⓐ wholesome
   Ⓑ laughable
   Ⓒ poor
   Ⓓ offensive

© SSI • DO NOT DUPLICATE

8. The bank would stand for no **improprieties** from the tellers when it came to the way they handled their cash.

   A mistakes

   B accidents

   C decorum

   D recommendations

9. Mark was **penitent** about forgetting to pick up his grandparents at the airport.

   A angry

   B tranquil

   C unsure

   D unapologetic

10. The intellectual edifice of art history has **accrued** over many years through the work of artists and scholars.

    A happened

    B prospered

    C wavered

    D decreased

Choose the best way to complete each sentence or answer each question. Then fill in the circle next to your answer.

11. Something with an **unsavory** aroma smells

    A sweet.

    B floral.

    C unpleasant.

    D delicious.

12. Which of the following is most likely to **accrue?**

    A beach erosion

    B freshly planted flowers

    C an infected wound

    D vacation time at a job

13. Nathan **inveigled** concert money from his mother by

    A flattery.

    B struggling.

    C threatening.

    D reasoning.

14. A **revelation** makes what was unknown

    A hidden.

    B forgotten.

    C irrelevant.

    D known.

15. **Purporting** to be related to someone means to

    A doubt your kinship.

    B suspect your kinship.

    C imply your kinship.

    D deny your kinship.

© SSI • DO NOT DUPLICATE

Standardized Test Preview/Practice

1. IMPROPRIETY : BELCHING ::

   Ⓐ revelation : surprise

   Ⓑ property : claim

   Ⓒ felony : kidnapping

   Ⓓ wave : hand

   Ⓔ rumor : gossiping

2. EXPLICIT : SUBTLETY ::

   Ⓐ rude : manners

   Ⓑ morbid : mausoleum

   Ⓒ hot : sweat

   Ⓓ lucky : fate

   Ⓔ ill : virus

3. One of the repercussions of the train accident was — in holiday travel.

   Ⓐ an extension

   Ⓑ a discount

   Ⓒ a boost

   Ⓓ an increase

   Ⓔ a decrease

4. Given her histrionic nature, it was no surprise that her — about the rumors that besmirched her reputation was —.

   Ⓐ reaction . . exaggerated

   Ⓑ sadness . . concealed

   Ⓒ anger . . contained

   Ⓓ excitement . . positive

   Ⓔ hysteria . . minor

5. Since she preferred not to deceive people, Beatriz showed — about inveigling her way into the invitation-only event.

   Ⓐ excitement

   Ⓑ nervousness

   Ⓒ eagerness

   Ⓓ confidence

   Ⓔ happiness

© SSI • DO NOT DUPLICATE

Lesson 6 ▸ Test

Find a SYNONYM for each bold word. Then fill in the circle next to your answer.

1. The father **assuaged** his baby's teething pain with some numbing drops.

   Ⓐ understood
   Ⓑ noticed
   Ⓒ angered
   Ⓓ relieved

2. The party's **convivial** atmosphere put Jacob right at ease.

   Ⓐ uncomfortable
   Ⓑ carnival
   Ⓒ sociable
   Ⓓ secretive

3. Jessie had her **eclectic** music collection to thank for landing her the DJ job.

   Ⓐ large
   Ⓑ specific
   Ⓒ varied
   Ⓓ ethnic

4. Charities rely on **munificent** contributions from private citizens as well as endowments from corporations.

   Ⓐ generous
   Ⓑ yearly
   Ⓒ steady
   Ⓓ public

5. His mother was known in the neighborhood for her **perspicacity** when advising on difficult matters.

   Ⓐ shrewdness
   Ⓑ bluntness
   Ⓒ understanding
   Ⓓ reassurance

Find an ANTONYM for each bold word. Then fill in the circle next to your answer.

6. There is something **intrinsic** to human biology that makes language possible for us, but not for chimpanzees.

   Ⓐ essential
   Ⓑ peripheral
   Ⓒ important
   Ⓓ valuable

7. Julian's **inveterate** tardiness angered his boss.

   Ⓐ inconsiderate
   Ⓑ bold
   Ⓒ occasional
   Ⓓ repeated

© SSI • DO NOT DUPLICATE

8. The plant's plentiful blooms were a **propitious** indication of Claire's potential as a gardener.

   Ⓐ ominous
   Ⓑ promising
   Ⓒ useless
   Ⓓ possible

9. Ringing cell phones were **anathema** to the theater's patrons.

   Ⓐ forbidden
   Ⓑ accessories
   Ⓒ distasteful
   Ⓓ welcome

10. The ointment **assuaged** the inflammation on Tim's skinned knee.

    Ⓐ increased
    Ⓑ disinfected
    Ⓒ soothed
    Ⓓ erased

Choose the best way to complete each sentence or answer each question. Then fill in the circle next to your answer.

11. To **expound** upon one's value system is to

    Ⓐ refuse to talk about it.
    Ⓑ use it for an argument.
    Ⓒ explain it in detail.
    Ⓓ expose its flaws.

12. Which of the following is most likely to be described as **nascent?**

    Ⓐ an adult
    Ⓑ a mountain
    Ⓒ a seedling
    Ⓓ a ripe apple

13. When George quoted an **epigram** of Oscar Wilde's, he repeated

    Ⓐ a speech.
    Ⓑ a lengthy poem.
    Ⓒ a biographic detail.
    Ⓓ a short saying.

14. Mr. Caddie's **philistine** attitude about the closing of the museum indicates that he is likely

    Ⓐ a museum supporter.
    Ⓑ interested in the arts.
    Ⓒ interested in the museum's fate.
    Ⓓ ignorant of artistic values.

15. The veterinarian calmed our fears with her **perspicacious** advice about the surgical procedure. The advice was

    Ⓐ confusing.
    Ⓑ late.
    Ⓒ clear-sighted.
    Ⓓ condescending.

© SSI • DO NOT DUPLICATE

Standardized Test Preview/Practice

1. PHILISTINE : INTELLECTUAL ::

   Ⓐ summer : cold

   Ⓑ doctor : medicinal

   Ⓒ vegetarian : carnivorous

   Ⓓ chef : frozen

   Ⓔ child : playful

2. MOGUL : POWER ::

   Ⓐ pauper : money

   Ⓑ acrobat : agility

   Ⓒ nurse : authority

   Ⓓ beautician : salary

   Ⓔ monster : terror

3. Although its intrinsic value was less than any other piece in her collection, the simple ring was her first gift from Uncle Alfredo, and it was one of Aunt Mayumi's — possessions.

   Ⓐ flashy

   Ⓑ tasteful

   Ⓒ utilitarian

   Ⓓ worthless

   Ⓔ prized

4. The clearing of the — was a propitious sign that they could sail that day.

   Ⓐ clouds

   Ⓑ schedule

   Ⓒ dock

   Ⓓ water

   Ⓔ rubbish

5. Despite his —, avuncular manner, Gwen's coach could not assuage her — about returning to the balance beam.

   Ⓐ reassuring .. eagerness

   Ⓑ kind .. ego

   Ⓒ harsh .. worry

   Ⓓ warm .. fears

   Ⓔ firm .. rush

© SSI • DO NOT DUPLICATE

Lesson 7 Test

Find a SYNONYM for each bold word. Then fill in the circle next to your answer.

1. Hal was not convinced he needed new tires until his car **careened** off a wet road.

   Ⓐ stalled
   Ⓑ swerved
   Ⓒ turned
   Ⓓ sped

2. Unusual behavior in animals has been known to **presage** earthquakes.

   Ⓐ predict
   Ⓑ prevent
   Ⓒ alleviate
   Ⓓ cause

3. The small sailboat **careened** in the rough sea.

   Ⓐ sank
   Ⓑ leaned
   Ⓒ swerved
   Ⓓ steadied

4. Even though his parents were adventurous cooks, Joe was **repulsed** by exotic foods.

   Ⓐ intrigued
   Ⓑ enchanted
   Ⓒ admired
   Ⓓ disgusted

5. Winning the lottery had **seismic** repercussions on Luke's life.

   Ⓐ powerful
   Ⓑ depressing
   Ⓒ tiny
   Ⓓ unforeseen

Find an ANTONYM for each bold word. Then fill in the circle next to your answer.

6. Because he had already decided to quit his job, Terry had a **cavalier** attitude towards punctuality.

   Ⓐ strict
   Ⓑ polite
   Ⓒ carefree
   Ⓓ humble

7. Astrophysics is a **recondite** subject of study for all but a few.

   Ⓐ simple
   Ⓑ complex
   Ⓒ popular
   Ⓓ collegiate

© SSI • DO NOT DUPLICATE

8. Anna **repulsed** the swarm of bees with a fumigator.

Ⓐ killed

Ⓑ attracted

Ⓒ disgusted

Ⓓ tamed

9. A crowd gathered to watch the wrecking ball **pulverize** the old apartment building.

Ⓐ touch

Ⓑ construct

Ⓒ demolish

Ⓓ damage

10. Ethel and Irving have visited all forty-eight **contiguous** states in their RV.

Ⓐ shared

Ⓑ close

Ⓒ separated

Ⓓ different

Choose the best way to complete each sentence or answer each question. Then fill in the circle next to your answer.

11. **Kinetic** energy is most related to

Ⓐ the sun.

Ⓑ water.

Ⓒ motion.

Ⓓ gravity.

12. After something is **pulverized,** what is most likely to remain?

Ⓐ evidence

Ⓑ garbage

Ⓒ liquid

Ⓓ dust

13. Warping from **upheaval** generally comes from what direction?

Ⓐ below

Ⓑ behind

Ⓒ above

Ⓓ sideways

14. How is a flag that is **undulating** moving?

Ⓐ falling

Ⓑ waving

Ⓒ whipping

Ⓓ snapping

15. How did Carolyn behave as she **repulsed** Allan's flirtatious advances?

Ⓐ cool

Ⓑ friendly

Ⓒ cheerful

Ⓓ flattered

© SSI • DO NOT DUPLICATE

Standardized Test Preview/Practice

1. The Baltic archipelago contains several — that I hope to visit someday soon.

   Ⓐ attractions

   Ⓑ countries

   Ⓒ restaurants

   Ⓓ islands

   Ⓔ museums

2. The dietician informed me about the correlation between — and drinking milk.

   Ⓐ strong bones

   Ⓑ bad breath

   Ⓒ acne

   Ⓓ wit

   Ⓔ good eyesight

3. The seismic vibrations of the underwater — triggered undulations in the ocean surface, with — reaching dangerous sizes.

   Ⓐ earthquake . . waves

   Ⓑ volcano . . blasts

   Ⓒ whirlpool . . rotations

   Ⓓ discovery . . treasure

   Ⓔ struggle . . aggression

4. UPHEAVAL : RADICAL ::

   Ⓐ development : impatient

   Ⓑ incremental : growth

   Ⓒ evolution : gradual

   Ⓓ glacial : progress

   Ⓔ erosion : fleeting

5. ETYMOLOGY : WORDS ::

   Ⓐ crockery : pans

   Ⓑ geology : stars

   Ⓒ Egyptology : history

   Ⓓ weather : earthquakes

   Ⓔ zoology : animals

© SSI • DO NOT DUPLICATE

Name _____   Date _____

Lesson 8 > Test

Find a SYNONYM for each bold word. Then fill in the circle next to your answer.

1. Though some doubted their authenticity, scholars have verified Mark Twain's lost writings and included them in his **canon.**

   Ⓐ estate
   Ⓑ writing
   Ⓒ library
   Ⓓ catalog

2. Grandmother hoped that James would ask Mari to be his **betrothed.**

   Ⓐ fiancée
   Ⓑ mentor
   Ⓒ roommate
   Ⓓ date

3. The **cadence** of dozens of joggers moving together helps Dan stay energized for the long race.

   Ⓐ sound
   Ⓑ rhythm
   Ⓒ excitement
   Ⓓ distraction

4. During surgery, the patient will be **insensate.**

   Ⓐ energized
   Ⓑ swollen
   Ⓒ unaware
   Ⓓ sensitive

5. Justin found it difficult to adjust to the **strictures** of military life.

   Ⓐ limitations
   Ⓑ routine
   Ⓒ opportunities
   Ⓓ challenges

Find an ANTONYM for each bold word. Then fill in the circle next to your answer.

6. After staying awake all night studying, Morris was **insensate** when the time came to take the test.

   Ⓐ tired
   Ⓑ dizzy
   Ⓒ sleeping
   Ⓓ aware

7. Many accused the students of **blasphemy** for painting graffiti over the stained glass window in the church.

   Ⓐ crimes
   Ⓑ disrespect
   Ⓒ reverence
   Ⓓ insanity

© SSI • DO NOT DUPLICATE

8. Detecting a rift among the cabinet ministers, the general decided to use force to **usurp** power from the civilian authority.

Ⓐ restore

Ⓑ seize

Ⓒ win

Ⓓ challenge

9. Molly was never timid with her **strictures** about trends in fashion.

Ⓐ objections

Ⓑ opinions

Ⓒ criticisms

Ⓓ endorsements

10. In his closing argument, the attorney offered a **soliloquy** about his theory of the crime.

Ⓐ dialogue

Ⓑ apology

Ⓒ oration

Ⓓ description

Choose the best way to complete each sentence or answer each question. Then fill in the circle next to your answer.

11. In which class are you most likely to discuss a **denouement?**

Ⓐ literature

Ⓑ geography

Ⓒ biology

Ⓓ geometry

12. Where are you most likely to find a **soliloquy?**

Ⓐ in a vault

Ⓑ in a garage

Ⓒ in an archive

Ⓓ in a play

13. Which of the following is most likely to be described as a **renegade?**

Ⓐ a farmer

Ⓑ an entrepreneur

Ⓒ a double agent

Ⓓ a journalist

14. Which of the following most closely describes an **edict?**

Ⓐ request

Ⓑ command

Ⓒ threat

Ⓓ guideline

15. A **votary** of a cause has what relationship to that cause?

Ⓐ devotion

Ⓑ indifference

Ⓒ leadership

Ⓓ administrative

© SSI • DO NOT DUPLICATE

Standardized Test Preview/Practice

1. ROBE : VESTMENT ::

   Ⓐ spoon : ladle

   Ⓑ clothing : shirt

   Ⓒ violin : instrument

   Ⓓ anger : violence

   Ⓔ clouds : sky

2. USURP : AUTHORITY ::

   Ⓐ cook : food

   Ⓑ rent : property

   Ⓒ freeze : ice

   Ⓓ conceal : plunder

   Ⓔ embezzle : money

3. Russell and Kim were — enamored with each other, so we were — when they were betrothed.

   Ⓐ totally . . worried

   Ⓑ casually . . thrilled

   Ⓒ mildly . . bored

   Ⓓ obviously . . happy

   Ⓔ deeply . . shocked

4. Lina felt it was insensate of the teacher to subject the class to such a dull lecture in the slow, steady cadence of his —.

   Ⓐ slides

   Ⓑ voice

   Ⓒ assignments

   Ⓓ footsteps

   Ⓔ questions

5. Tax evasion clearly — the accepted canons of ethics for an accountant.

   Ⓐ respects

   Ⓑ obeys

   Ⓒ violates

   Ⓓ accepts

   Ⓔ attacks

© SSI • DO NOT DUPLICATE

Lesson 9 ▷ Test

Find a SYNONYM for each bold word. Then fill in the circle next to your answer.

1. The loops of the roller coaster made me **queasy.**

   Ⓐ frightened
   Ⓑ nauseous
   Ⓒ angry
   Ⓓ quiet

2. After enjoying the hospitality of friends, it is nice to **reciprocate** as soon as possible.

   Ⓐ repay
   Ⓑ thank
   Ⓒ praise
   Ⓓ ignore

3. Eduardo enjoyed **fabricating** model airplanes from kits.

   Ⓐ flying
   Ⓑ buying
   Ⓒ building
   Ⓓ displaying

4. Jake's reluctance to fly borders on being a **phobia.**

   Ⓐ quirk
   Ⓑ fear
   Ⓒ aversion
   Ⓓ allergy

5. It requires a great deal of **bravado** to participate in professional wrestling.

   Ⓐ skill
   Ⓑ strength
   Ⓒ bravery
   Ⓓ resilience

Find an ANTONYM for each bold word. Then fill in the circle next to your answer.

6. Charlotte annoyed her friends by being **blasé** about meeting the president.

   Ⓐ excited
   Ⓑ indifferent
   Ⓒ calm
   Ⓓ secretive

7. Even though he deserved it, Robbie was **queasy** at the thought of asking for a raise.

   Ⓐ nervous
   Ⓑ calm
   Ⓒ arrogant
   Ⓓ ill

© SSI • DO NOT DUPLICATE

8. We **relegated** the matter of dispersing the budget surplus to the subcommittee for a vote.

   Ⓐ assigned
   Ⓑ demoted
   Ⓒ mentioned
   Ⓓ withheld

9. Maria and Lou worked out a **reciprocal** agreement that allowed them both one night of babysitting and one night of leisure every weekend.

   Ⓐ balanced
   Ⓑ unfair
   Ⓒ one-sided
   Ⓓ secret

10. Mr. Anderson's **proclivity** for essay assignments made him an intimidating teacher for some students.

    Ⓐ inclination
    Ⓑ aversion
    Ⓒ talent
    Ⓓ fondness

Choose the best way to complete each sentence or answer each question. Then fill in the circle next to your answer.

11. Which saying best reflects **reciprocity?**

    Ⓐ Do unto others as you would have them do unto you.
    Ⓑ A stitch in time saves nine.
    Ⓒ A bird in the hand is worth two in the bush.
    Ⓓ An ounce of prevention is worth a pound of cure.

12. Which of the following is the best example of a **domicile?**

    Ⓐ a library
    Ⓑ an apartment
    Ⓒ a gym
    Ⓓ an office

13. To make something appear **lilliputian** is to make it seem

    Ⓐ tiny.
    Ⓑ fierce.
    Ⓒ fast.
    Ⓓ important.

14. Trey looked for a **projectile** to scare the approaching badger. Trey wanted something to

    Ⓐ burn.
    Ⓑ brandish.
    Ⓒ eat.
    Ⓓ throw.

15. If a club's membership is **disparate,** it is most likely

    Ⓐ small.
    Ⓑ diverse.
    Ⓒ widespread.
    Ⓓ uniform.

© SSI • DO NOT DUPLICATE

Standardized Test Preview/Practice

1. VERTIGO : DIZZY ::

   Ⓐ transportation : swift

   Ⓑ pineapple : fruity

   Ⓒ ocean : vast

   Ⓓ melancholy : sad

   Ⓔ disease : hopeful

2. DOMICILE : DWELL ::

   Ⓐ shovel : dirt

   Ⓑ car : luxury

   Ⓒ mansion : shack

   Ⓓ trip : fall

   Ⓔ bed : sleep

3. The advent of the personal computer meant the — of the typewriter.

   Ⓐ competition

   Ⓑ decline

   Ⓒ acceptance

   Ⓓ scarcity

   Ⓔ resurgence

4. A — is likely to be described as lilliputian.

   Ⓐ cow

   Ⓑ bicycle

   Ⓒ sofa

   Ⓓ thimble

   Ⓔ hat

5. As an itinerant social worker for the United Nations, Tabitha had — the disparity between the lifestyles of the world's richest and — people.

   Ⓐ experienced . . wealthiest

   Ⓑ witnessed . . poorest

   Ⓒ revealed . . powerful

   Ⓓ described . . famous

   Ⓔ announced . . healthiest

© SSI • DO NOT DUPLICATE

Lesson **10** Test

Find a SYNONYM for each bold word. Then fill in the circle next to your answer.

1. Her sister suggested that flowers might **appease** Tomiko's anger.

   Ⓐ pacify
   Ⓑ increase
   Ⓒ defer
   Ⓓ remove

2. Raphael is an award-winning **equestrian.**

   Ⓐ journalist
   Ⓑ designer
   Ⓒ rider
   Ⓓ fundraiser

3. Because of her efforts to catch up, Pia's absences were **expunged** from the records.

   Ⓐ erased
   Ⓑ worsened
   Ⓒ average
   Ⓓ changed

4. Many people lost their savings in the stock market **debacle.**

   Ⓐ struggle
   Ⓑ failure
   Ⓒ controversy
   Ⓓ rumor

5. After being caught cheating in the student government election, Loren experienced **opprobrium** from her teachers and classmates.

   Ⓐ loss
   Ⓑ embarrassment
   Ⓒ contempt
   Ⓓ lessons

Find an ANTONYM for each bold word. Then fill in the circle next to your answer.

6. Brandy **upbraided** Michele for her selfishness.

   Ⓐ thanked
   Ⓑ scolded
   Ⓒ ignored
   Ⓓ praised

7. Billboards **sullied** what used to be a beautiful, scenic drive.

   Ⓐ dotted
   Ⓑ improved
   Ⓒ ruined
   Ⓓ developed

© SSI • DO NOT DUPLICATE

8. After a long day's hike, our team reached the **vertex** of Mount Rainier.

   Ⓐ summit
   Ⓑ middle
   Ⓒ slope
   Ⓓ base

9. The **attrition** of technology jobs in the slowing economy led to increased unemployment claims.

   Ⓐ difficulty
   Ⓑ addition
   Ⓒ loss
   Ⓓ salaries

10. The tour manager attempted to **appease** the restless crowd by bringing out the opening act.

    Ⓐ enrage
    Ⓑ repay
    Ⓒ usurp
    Ⓓ excite

Choose the best way to complete each sentence or answer each question. Then fill in the circle next to your answer.

11. My cousin Ladarius has **amnesia** from his head injury and can tell us

    Ⓐ details about the accident.
    Ⓑ nothing about the accident.
    Ⓒ everything about the accident.
    Ⓓ his memories about the accident.

12. Which of the following is most likely to appear **verdant?**

    Ⓐ a clear sky
    Ⓑ a mud puddle
    Ⓒ vanilla ice cream
    Ⓓ a field of clover

13. With what is a **tactile** sensation most likely experienced?

    Ⓐ your imagination
    Ⓑ your hands
    Ⓒ your eyes
    Ⓓ your nose

14. In a struggle of **attrition,** one side tries to defeat the other through what means?

    Ⓐ harassment
    Ⓑ reason
    Ⓒ lies
    Ⓓ the law

15. **Equestrian** sports involve

    Ⓐ guns.
    Ⓑ ice.
    Ⓒ endurance.
    Ⓓ horses.

© SSI • DO NOT DUPLICATE

Standardized Test Preview/Practice

1. Charles, the gardener, took great care to — his — from parasites that might defoliate them.

    Ⓐ protect . . trees
    Ⓑ guard . . chemicals
    Ⓒ endanger . . shrubs
    Ⓓ store . . tools
    Ⓔ prune . . flowers

2. The contract contained a proviso to — the scope of the agreement.

    Ⓐ dampen
    Ⓑ illuminate
    Ⓒ define
    Ⓓ restrict
    Ⓔ broaden

3. AMNESIA : MEMORY ::

    Ⓐ diet : cookies
    Ⓑ cards : game
    Ⓒ rebel : authority
    Ⓓ blindness : sight
    Ⓔ grain : wheat

4. With his hackneyed expressions, Pietro was no competition for more — essayists.

    Ⓐ practiced
    Ⓑ original
    Ⓒ predictable
    Ⓓ technical
    Ⓔ emotional

5. Amidst the beautiful verdant —, Ariel was able to expunge any —.

    Ⓐ architecture . . memory
    Ⓑ landscape . . worries
    Ⓒ dresses . . doubt
    Ⓓ sailboats . . nausea
    Ⓔ sculpture . . debt

© SSI • DO NOT DUPLICATE

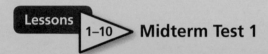

Read the passage. Choose the best answer for each sentence or question about a bold word. Then fill in the circle next to your answer.

Extra, Extra! Read All About It!

In Renaissance Europe, handwritten newsletters circulated privately among merchants who passed along information about everything from wars and economic conditions to social customs and stories of human interest. With the **advent** of the printing press came the first printed forerunners of the newspaper. These documents appeared in Germany in the late 1400s in the form of news pamphlets called "broadsides." The earliest American newspapers developed to spread news of colonial political concerns as well as to report on events of local interest. These early newspapers were produced for **opulent,** highly educated people who could afford the yearly subscriptions.

The growth of colonial newspapers **correlated** with the growing belief that information should be independent from governmental control. Newspaper publishers in the 17th and 18th centuries played more than just a **peripheral** role in the colonies' decision to break from England. Their struggle to be free from English control helped shape the concept of an independent press. As early as 1690, colonial newspapers sought **autonomy,** yet publishers relied on the **munificence** of Britain for printing the paper. The council of the Massachusetts Bay Colony approved all content. The British government found the idea of an independent colonial newspaper **disconcerting.** In 1721, Benjamin Franklin's older brother James published items in his paper, *The New-England Courant,* without the official seal of the government. The British government considered him a **renegade** and jailed him like a common criminal.

In 1833, Benjamin Day created the first successful "penny paper"—a newspaper that published advertising to decrease the cost to customers. Day's paper, the *New York Sun*, published sensationalized news and reported local gossip. Readers could now buy papers daily rather than pay the one lump sum of a subscription. Day also hired newsboys, who would employ **histrionics** to interest people in the news. People would buy papers as newsboys stood on busy street corners and shouted the headlines to passersby.

Many early newspapers failed, but **perspicacious** investors could see the potential for growth in the industry. Newspaper publishing ventures soon turned profitable as the popularity of newspapers spread to communities of immigrants and people on the frontier. In the antebellum South and beyond, African American newspapers expressed the need for social change. Ethnic and Native American newspapers met the needs of a growing America. Specialty papers like the *North Star*, founded by abolitionist leader Frederick Douglass, became voices against the **thralldom** of blacks and women.

The **nascent** women's movement gained a minor toehold in the beginning of the 18th century. In 1738, Elizabeth Timothy took over editing responsibilities for the *South Carolina Gazette* after the death of her husband. She is recognized today as the first female American

© SSI • DO NOT DUPLICATE

newspaper editor. Other notable examples of female pioneers in the publishing industry include Anna Zenger, a proponent of free press, and journalist Ida B. Wells, a crusader for civil rights.

Newspapers have played an important role in America's social environment since colonial times. The colonial press led the quest for national independence by **inculcating** the public with strident messages of political injustice and unrest. Two hundred years later, social activists of the 1960s resurrected the idea of newspapers as a voice of the downtrodden in America. Even today, in an era of high-speed electronic communication, newspapers still create a sense of community for the people they serve.

1. Which of the following would be least likely to be described as **peripheral?**

   Ⓐ whole
   Ⓑ center
   Ⓒ edge
   Ⓓ boundary

2. In the fifth paragraph, **nascent** is a SYNONYM for all of the following EXCEPT which?

   Ⓐ budding
   Ⓑ emerging
   Ⓒ arising
   Ⓓ dwindling

3. **Histrionics** is most closely related to behavior that is

   Ⓐ laudable.
   Ⓑ theatrical.
   Ⓒ calming.
   Ⓓ dignified.

4. Which of the following is most closely related to **thralldom?**

   Ⓐ freedom
   Ⓑ fascination
   Ⓒ slavery
   Ⓓ illness

© SSI • DO NOT DUPLICATE

5. Who are people least likely to be described as **opulent,** as the word is used in the passage?

   Ⓐ royalty

   Ⓑ tycoons

   Ⓒ servants

   Ⓓ celebrities

6. As used in the passage, **perspicacious** means

   Ⓐ selfish.

   Ⓑ apt.

   Ⓒ wealthy.

   Ⓓ shrewd.

7. If two things are **correlated,** they are

   Ⓐ different.

   Ⓑ related.

   Ⓒ similar.

   Ⓓ complex.

8. As used in paragraph two, **disconcerting** most closely means

   Ⓐ upsetting.

   Ⓑ engaging.

   Ⓒ understanding.

   Ⓓ intriguing.

9. All of the following are SYNONYMS for the word **renegade,** as it is used in the passage, EXCEPT which?

   Ⓐ rebel

   Ⓑ criminal

   Ⓒ traitor

   Ⓓ hero

10. An ANTONYM for **munificence** is

   Ⓐ selfishness.

   Ⓑ influence.

   Ⓒ generosity.

   Ⓓ stinginess.

© SSI • DO NOT DUPLICATE

Standardized Test Preview/Practice

1. In the first paragraph, **advent** most nearly means

   (A) arrival.

   (B) popularity.

   (C) changes.

   (D) promises.

   (E) problems.

2. To teach by **inculcating** most likely involves what?

   (A) experiments

   (B) debate

   (C) memorization

   (D) repetition

   (E) essays

3. **Autonomy** most closely means

   (A) independence.

   (B) reliance.

   (C) possibility.

   (D) intelligence.

   (E) embellishment.

4. A character that plays a **peripheral** role in a drama is

   (A) driving the action.

   (B) affected by the action.

   (C) not central to the action.

   (D) opposed to the action.

   (E) a victim of the action.

5. Which of the following pairs is most likely to be found to have a **correlation?**

   (A) height and eye color

   (B) nutrition and health

   (C) rhythm and blues

   (D) apples and oranges

   (E) wealth and happiness

© SSI • DO NOT DUPLICATE

© SSI • DO NOT DUPLICATE

Midterm Test 2

Read the passage. Choose the best answer for each sentence or question about a bold word. Then fill in the circle next to your answer.

The United Nations Fights for Peace

The history of mankind has been a history of military, social, and economic battles between groups of people. For thousands of years, clans have fought clans, tribes have fought tribes, and nations have fought nations for control of important resources. In the early 20th century, however, Europe was devastated by World War I. This war was so destructive and horrific that heads of state and the general populace alike began to press for peaceful cooperation among the countries of the world.

The first attempt at international cooperation was the formation of the League of Nations. The League was established in 1919 under the Treaty of Versailles, which ended World War I. Unfortunately, the League of Nations failed to prevent World War II, another catastrophic war. This **debacle** encouraged the U.S. and its allies to establish the United Nations. The name "United Nations" was first used by United States President Franklin D. Roosevelt in January 1942 during the war, when representatives of 26 nations pledged their governments' support in the fight against the Axis powers. The UN was created to stabilize international relations, secure rules of warfare, and promote and develop policies for settling crises peacefully.

In Moscow on October 30, 1943, the **disparate** governments of the Soviet Union, the United Kingdom, the United States, and China called for an early establishment of an international organization to maintain peace and security. That goal was reaffirmed at the meeting of the leaders of the United States, the Soviet Union, and the United Kingdom in Tehran on December 1, 1943. The United Nations charter was ratified on October 24, 1945. The organization officially **convened** on January 24, 1946. Amid the threat of nuclear war, **strictures** from world leaders, and seemingly endless conflicts caused by those trying to **usurp** power, peacekeeping has become an overriding concern of the United Nations. Dictators who **ensconce** themselves in the halls of power and then violate their citizens' rights can expect to face censure from the UN. The UN has been instrumental in trying to help the world achieve peace and security.

In its relatively brief history, the United Nations has had many decorated leaders. From 1997 to 2006, the UN was led by Secretary-General Kofi Annan. A native of Ghana, Annan was the first diplomat to rise to secretary-general from within the international civil service. He was also the first African elected to the post. During his career, Annan had been **indoctrinated** in UN policy, performing important assignments in the field and at duty stations throughout the world, beginning with a position in the World Heath Organization in 1962. As Secretary-General, Kofi Annan was instrumental in bringing new life to an organization previously **relegated** largely to ceremonial displays. Annan's first major initiative was his plan for reform, "Renewing the United Nations." The plan emphasized improving coherence and coordination in the organization. It was Annan's goal to ensure that the **edicts** of the United Nations

were binding on all members, and that the UN's power to promote peace and economic development was not undermined by the aggression of a single country.

Annan was succeeded in 2007 by Ban Ki-moon, the Minister of Foreign Affairs and Trade for the Republic of South Korea. Mr. Ban had worked for the UN in several capacities. He had served as chairman of the Preparatory Commission for the Nuclear Test Ban treaty of 2001–2002. He also headed the South Korean Republic's Presidency of the General Assembly. In the latter role Mr. Ban was instrumental in leading the official UN condemnation of the 2001 attacks on the World Trade Center in New York City.

With the **denouement** of the Cold War and the rise in terrorism around the world, the UN has been called on to more fully perform its mission to provide a forum for conflict resolution. That said, the United Nations and its family of agencies are still engaged in an **eclectic** array of work that touches every aspect of people's lives around the world. Primary initiatives of this office include providing adequate health care and nutrition to needy world citizens, protecting human rights, and maintaining the environment.

In addressing environmental concerns, Ban Ki-moon presided over the historic 2009 climate change conference in Copenhagen, Denmark. His message for the conference was direct. "Now is the time to act," he said. "Seldom in history has a choice been so clear. We can move toward a future of sustainable green growth, or we can continue down the road to ruin."

The UN remains determined to meet the world's economic, social, and environmental challenges. It will continue to tackle the issues of health and medical research, environmental protection, and human rights. As **votaries** of peace, then-leader Kofi Annan and the United Nations received the Nobel Peace Prize on December 10, 2001, "for their work for a better organized and more peaceful world."

1. As used in the second paragraph, all of the following are SYNONYMS for **debacle** EXCEPT

   Ⓐ failure.
   Ⓑ downfall.
   Ⓒ collapse.
   Ⓓ setback.

2. As used in the third paragraph, **disparate** refers to what kinds of things?

   Ⓐ allied
   Ⓑ similar
   Ⓒ different
   Ⓓ warring

3. As used in the third paragraph, a SYNONYM for **convened** is

   Ⓐ organized.
   Ⓑ gathered.
   Ⓒ dissolved.
   Ⓓ opened.

© SSI · DO NOT DUPLICATE

4. As used in the third paragraph, **strictures** is most closely related to

Ⓐ requests.

Ⓑ objections.

Ⓒ demands.

Ⓓ criticisms.

5. As used in this passage, a SYNONYM for **usurp** is

Ⓐ share.

Ⓑ abdicate.

Ⓒ seize.

Ⓓ win.

6. As used in the fourth paragraph, all of the following are SYNONYMS for **indoctrinated** EXCEPT

Ⓐ instilled.

Ⓑ taught.

Ⓒ trained.

Ⓓ brainwashed.

7. As used in this passage, **ensconce** is most closely related to being

Ⓐ uncomfortable.

Ⓑ secure.

Ⓒ hesitant.

Ⓓ shy.

8. **Relegated,** as used in the fourth paragraph, is most closely related to being

Ⓐ demoted.

Ⓑ assigned.

Ⓒ promoted.

Ⓓ concerned.

9. As used in the sixth paragraph, **denouement** most nearly means

Ⓐ horror.

Ⓑ triumph.

Ⓒ end.

Ⓓ outcome.

10. As used in the sixth paragraph, **eclectic** refers to all of the following except

Ⓐ assortment.

Ⓑ variety.

Ⓒ uniformity.

Ⓓ range.

© SSI • DO NOT DUPLICATE

Standardized Test Preview/Practice

1. In the eighth paragraph, **votaries** is least related to

   Ⓐ commitment.

   Ⓑ devotion.

   Ⓒ fickleness.

   Ⓓ loyalty.

   Ⓔ allegiance.

2. As used in the fourth paragraph, an **edict** is most closely related to

   Ⓐ a pact.

   Ⓑ a treaty.

   Ⓒ a letter.

   Ⓓ a guide.

   Ⓔ a decree.

3. Which of the following is most likely to describe a **debacle?**

   Ⓐ sudden

   Ⓑ minor

   Ⓒ gradual

   Ⓓ partial

   Ⓔ destroyed

4. Which of the following is most likely to be **convened?**

   Ⓐ a movie

   Ⓑ a sporting event

   Ⓒ a vacation

   Ⓓ a party

   Ⓔ a meeting

5. Which of the following is least likely to contain an **eclectic** assortment of things?

   Ⓐ a fruit basket

   Ⓑ a department store

   Ⓒ a tire shop

   Ⓓ a backpack

   Ⓔ a museum

© SSI • DO NOT DUPLICATE

Lesson 11 ▷ Test

Find a SYNONYM for each bold word. Then fill in the circle next to your answer.

1. Covering her mouth and nose with a scarf, Lori tried to **attenuate** the harshness of the bitter cold air.

    Ⓐ decrease
    Ⓑ warm
    Ⓒ increase
    Ⓓ avoid

2. Sunday noise ordinances **impinged** on residents' rights to tend to their yards during their time off from work.

    Ⓐ allowed
    Ⓑ overlooked
    Ⓒ threatened
    Ⓓ encroached

3. It struck Raul as an **oxymoron** when Shana told him to "act naturally."

    Ⓐ contradiction
    Ⓑ impossibility
    Ⓒ joke
    Ⓓ insult

4. Chris annoyed his friends by assuming "Work now; play later" was a **postulate** they all accepted.

    Ⓐ ethic
    Ⓑ guideline
    Ⓒ goal
    Ⓓ principle

5. Jason only makes his famous peach pie in late summer, because he refuses to use fruit that is not perfectly **succulent.**

    Ⓐ grown
    Ⓑ juicy
    Ⓒ ready
    Ⓓ aromatic

Find an ANTONYM for each bold word. Then fill in the circle next to your answer.

6. The chef's skilled fingers made it look effortless to **attenuate** the dough into long ropes to be cut into spaghetti.

    Ⓐ stretch
    Ⓑ shape
    Ⓒ fatten
    Ⓓ roll

7. Rumors that his death was faked circulated for a century before the family allowed his body to be **disinterred** and proven to be that of Jesse James.

    Ⓐ disturbed
    Ⓑ buried
    Ⓒ tested
    Ⓓ identified

© SSI • DO NOT DUPLICATE

8. When it came to appeasing Nat's sweet tooth, ice cream would **prevail** over cake every time.

   (A) win
   (B) dominate
   (C) lose
   (D) weaken

9. When Juan's parents asked if he would like to spend his junior year abroad, he responded with an **unequivocal** "yes."

   (A) ambiguous
   (B) ungrateful
   (C) emotional
   (D) hysterical

10. Diana was accustomed to her small car, and she found it difficult to adjust to driving a **behemoth** like her friend's van.

    (A) vehicle
    (B) size
    (C) car
    (D) miniature

Choose the best way to complete each sentence or answer each question. Then fill in the circle next to your answer.

11. A large tree **impinged** on our porch roof during the storm. The tree

    (A) threatened it.
    (B) blew off it.
    (C) crashed on it.
    (D) cast a shadow on it.

12. How much do you have when you have a **plenitude** of something?

    (A) a shortage
    (B) enough
    (C) an abundance
    (D) an excess

13. What can be said of a trend that **prevails?**

    (A) It is widespread.
    (B) It is new.
    (C) It is weakening.
    (D) It is over.

14. Which sense is offended by something that has **putrefied?**

    (A) sight
    (B) smell
    (C) touch
    (D) hearing

15. Which of the following most nearly relates to **vicissitudes?**

    (A) incisions
    (B) food
    (C) fluctuations
    (D) travel

© SSI · DO NOT DUPLICATE

Standardized Test Preview/Practice

1. MULTIFARIOUS : VARIETY ::

    Ⓐ ingenious : thought

    Ⓑ quadrilateral : symmetry

    Ⓒ sinister : deception

    Ⓓ uniform : sameness

    Ⓔ bilateral : side

2. SALUBRIOUS : HEALTH ::

    Ⓐ toxic : illness

    Ⓑ ugly : horror

    Ⓒ kind : bliss

    Ⓓ rare : treasure

    Ⓔ common : abundance

3. Grandmother is going to — this summer to fulfill her lifelong dream of riding a dogsled across the tundra.

    Ⓐ Nigeria

    Ⓑ Australia

    Ⓒ Italy

    Ⓓ Alaska

    Ⓔ Brazil

4. Based on the ancient — disinterred from the dig in Egypt, archaeologists postulated that the person — there had been very important.

    Ⓐ restaurant . . eating

    Ⓑ rituals . . sleeping

    Ⓒ germs . . working

    Ⓓ news . . living

    Ⓔ artifacts . . buried

5. The term — is a famous oxymoron.

    Ⓐ "puppy love"

    Ⓑ "dire situation"

    Ⓒ "discriminating taste"

    Ⓓ "civil war"

    Ⓔ "band practice"

© SSI • DO NOT DUPLICATE

Lesson 12 **Test**

Find a SYNONYM for each bold word. Then fill in the circle next to your answer.

1. Organizers were surprised at the **amity** with which former rivals worked when trying to achieve a common goal.

   Ⓐ difficulty
   Ⓑ hostility
   Ⓒ friendship
   Ⓓ friction

2. Emperor Commodus of Rome sought to **exalt** himself by giving himself twelve titles, then renaming the months of the year with those titles.

   Ⓐ glorify
   Ⓑ humiliate
   Ⓒ immortalize
   Ⓓ publicize

3. Though she was a millionaire many times over, Mitzi clung to her **penurious** ways.

   Ⓐ decadent
   Ⓑ careless
   Ⓒ evil
   Ⓓ stingy

4. Though the professional world knew her as Melissa Banks, Esq., she would never stop responding to the old family **sobriquet** "Mimi" when she was at home.

   Ⓐ nickname
   Ⓑ joke
   Ⓒ slogan
   Ⓓ cheer

5. While his father found the **bucolic** cabin restful, Adnan only considered it dull.

   Ⓐ cozy
   Ⓑ pastoral
   Ⓒ tiny
   Ⓓ remote

Find an ANTONYM for each bold word. Then fill in the circle next to your answer.

6. Jenna grew weary of Beth's constant **animadversions** and wished she would focus her energy on constructive comments.

   Ⓐ compliments
   Ⓑ criticisms
   Ⓒ gossip
   Ⓓ whining

7. Javin's ambition was to someday join the **exalted** ranks of the Nobel laureates.

   Ⓐ public
   Ⓑ secret
   Ⓒ lofty
   Ⓓ lowly

© SSI • DO NOT DUPLICATE

8. Marcia looked forward to graduating and getting a job, and the end of her **penurious** life as a college student.

    Ⓐ modest
    Ⓑ opulent
    Ⓒ frivolous
    Ⓓ innocent

9. Although they had not seen each other in almost five years, the **amity** between the cousins was as if they had never parted.

    Ⓐ hostility
    Ⓑ resemblance
    Ⓒ familiarity
    Ⓓ alienation

10. Jacob's friends would not let him forget his **craven** reaction to seeing the mouse run across the kitchen floor.

    Ⓐ animated
    Ⓑ brave
    Ⓒ comical
    Ⓓ stunned

Choose the best way to complete each sentence or answer each question. Then fill in the circle next to your answer.

11. When one person is another's **antithesis,** those people are each other's

    Ⓐ neighbors.
    Ⓑ family.
    Ⓒ friends.
    Ⓓ opposites.

12. Someone who is **craven** would be most likely to

    Ⓐ bake a cake.
    Ⓑ slay a dragon.
    Ⓒ hide from danger.
    Ⓓ build a tree house.

13. To **impugn** one's honesty is to

    Ⓐ call it into question.
    Ⓑ confirm it.
    Ⓒ make note of it.
    Ⓓ test it.

14. An **introspective** person is likely to be aware of his or her

    Ⓐ surroundings.
    Ⓑ feelings.
    Ⓒ enemies.
    Ⓓ belongings.

15. **Throes** are most likely to come from which of the following?

    Ⓐ pitchers
    Ⓑ surprises
    Ⓒ struggles
    Ⓓ windfalls

© SSI • DO NOT DUPLICATE

Standardized Test Preview/Practice

1. The Thomas twins were as antithetical as fire and —, and their — often created a bellicose atmosphere in their house.

   Ⓐ herbs . . tastes

   Ⓑ salt . . personalities

   Ⓒ olives . . agreements

   Ⓓ ice . . differences

   Ⓔ vinegar . . salad

2. INTROSPECTION : FEELINGS ::

   Ⓐ etymology : numbers

   Ⓑ investigation : evidence

   Ⓒ doctor : physical

   Ⓓ architect : carpenter

   Ⓔ lawyer : defendant

3. The privations of Mr. Roberts' — lifestyle revealed a penury that moved his neighbors to share their — with him.

   Ⓐ lavish . . weekends

   Ⓑ reckless . . advice

   Ⓒ worldly . . stories

   Ⓓ Spartan . . meals

   Ⓔ indulgent . . vacations

4. Laurie felt it was pointless to take the — aptitude test, since she was already certain that her metier would involve languages.

   Ⓐ scholastic

   Ⓑ career

   Ⓒ college

   Ⓓ future

   Ⓔ trade

5. Coach warned that — practice for the tournament was tantamount to forfeiting the title.

   Ⓐ inadequate

   Ⓑ excessive

   Ⓒ diligent

   Ⓓ committed

   Ⓔ respectful

© SSI • DO NOT DUPLICATE

Name _____   Date _____

Find a SYNONYM for each bold word. Then fill in the circle next to your answer.

1. The actress could not choose between the prestigious Broadway part and her regular television role, so she opted to appear in both of the **concurrent** productions.

   Ⓐ popular
   Ⓑ disparate
   Ⓒ simultaneous
   Ⓓ demanding

2. Tabloid newspapers often change the meaning of a statement by presenting it without providing the **context** in which it originally occurred.

   Ⓐ circumstances
   Ⓑ mood
   Ⓒ meaning
   Ⓓ reaction

3. Liz declined the invitation, since she knew the heat of Ceylonese **cuisine** was more than she could take.

   Ⓐ beaches
   Ⓑ theaters
   Ⓒ saunas
   Ⓓ cooking

4. A traffic citation **enjoins** the recipient to pay a fine or to appear in court.

   Ⓐ forbids
   Ⓑ commands
   Ⓒ requests
   Ⓓ prohibits

5. The **genesis** for Erik's business idea was when Pat mentioned that he did not want a pet, but that he wanted a dog to run with.

   Ⓐ origin
   Ⓑ outcome
   Ⓒ result
   Ⓓ success

Find an ANTONYM for each bold word. Then fill in the circle next to your answer.

6. Though the same could not necessarily be said of his business practices, Andrew Carnegie's private **altruism** was legendary.

   Ⓐ selfishness
   Ⓑ generosity
   Ⓒ immaturity
   Ⓓ charity

7. Since Martin could not seem to refrain from making **crass** comments, I decided not to bring him to the wedding.

   Ⓐ serious
   Ⓑ loud
   Ⓒ tasteless
   Ⓓ delicate

© SSI • DO NOT DUPLICATE

8. Rather than **debase** the office with a long, sordid inquiry, Rachel chose to resign quietly.

Ⓐ expose

Ⓑ glorify

Ⓒ cheapen

Ⓓ preoccupy

9. Kathryn could not seem to **reconcile** herself to the fact that her mother's promotion meant changing schools for her senior year.

Ⓐ resist

Ⓑ accept

Ⓒ admit

Ⓓ realize

10. Padraig would remember the emergency of the mudslide as the **genesis** of his career in medicine.

Ⓐ inspiration

Ⓑ end

Ⓒ highlight

Ⓓ birth

Choose the best way to complete each sentence or answer each question. Then fill in the circle next to your answer.

11. If students are **enjoined** from leaving campus during school hours, that means that they are

Ⓐ permitted to leave campus.

Ⓑ encouraged to leave campus.

Ⓒ forbidden to leave campus.

Ⓓ discouraged from leaving campus.

12. Before an **extemporaneous** speech, which of the following is Cherrie most likely to do?

Ⓐ clear her throat

Ⓑ prepare note cards

Ⓒ rehearse with a friend

Ⓓ memorize the outline

13. When Janice is experiencing a **malaise,** she feels

Ⓐ joyful.

Ⓑ energetic.

Ⓒ ill.

Ⓓ elated.

14. If neighbors need to **reconcile,** then they are currently

Ⓐ amicable.

Ⓑ feuding.

Ⓒ cordial.

Ⓓ blaming.

15. The stock market crash of 1929 led to a decade of **travail.** Which of the following least describes **travail?**

Ⓐ suffering

Ⓑ anguish

Ⓒ hardship

Ⓓ inactivity

© SSI • DO NOT DUPLICATE

Standardized Test Preview/Practice

1. CONTEXT : WORD ::

   Ⓐ office : party

   Ⓑ habitat : animal

   Ⓒ jury : courtroom

   Ⓓ lion : zoo

   Ⓔ dormitory : college

2. LIBATIONS : LIQUIDS ::

   Ⓐ wool : sweater

   Ⓑ trousers : pleats

   Ⓒ vegetables : fruits

   Ⓓ monkeys : primates

   Ⓔ prayers : church

3. When asked to — extemporaneously at the Rotary Club luncheon, the candidate became so flustered that she could think of nothing — to say and had to resort to platitudes.

   Ⓐ speak . . original

   Ⓑ perform . . relevant

   Ⓒ rally . . pressing

   Ⓓ campaign . . compelling

   Ⓔ appear . . else

4. Jealousy sundered the sisters' — years ago, but the family — they would reconcile for their parents' anniversary.

   Ⓐ feelings . . suspected

   Ⓑ relationship . . hoped

   Ⓒ futures . . doubted

   Ⓓ homes . . wished

   Ⓔ egos . . believed

5. Part of Carl's contradictory nature was that he enjoyed —, but never enjoyed ethnic cuisines.

   Ⓐ takeout

   Ⓑ meatloaf

   Ⓒ travel

   Ⓓ delicacies

   Ⓔ sweets

© SSI • DO NOT DUPLICATE

Lesson 14 ▷ Test

Find a SYNONYM for each bold word. Then fill in the circle next to your answer.

1. Ross **buttressed** his argument that he deserved a promotion by charting sales increases in the years since he was first hired.

   Ⓐ proved
   Ⓑ strengthened
   Ⓒ illustrated
   Ⓓ punctuated

2. To enhance cultural awareness, the community center set up an **ecumenical** center and encouraged discussions there.

   Ⓐ international
   Ⓑ open
   Ⓒ selective
   Ⓓ universal

3. No matter what shock she encountered in her work as a counselor, Coretta kept it hidden behind her blasé **facade.**

   Ⓐ appearance
   Ⓑ smile
   Ⓒ personality
   Ⓓ eyeglasses

4. The advent of World War II made the debate about whether it was appropriate for women to work outside the home **moot.**

   Ⓐ irrelevant
   Ⓑ heated
   Ⓒ important
   Ⓓ accelerate

5. Wayne chose not to battle the storm, but he vowed to see the **pinnacle** of Mt. Everest someday.

   Ⓐ snow
   Ⓑ view
   Ⓒ base
   Ⓓ peak

Find an ANTONYM for each bold word. Then fill in the circle next to your answer.

6. Barry was a hindrance to the group's progress, as he tended to be **dilatory** in completing his part of the work.

   Ⓐ thorough
   Ⓑ prompt
   Ⓒ dedicated
   Ⓓ sloppy

7. The topic of Claudia's curfew is **mooted** at the dinner table at least once weekly.

   Ⓐ discussed
   Ⓑ suggested
   Ⓒ debated
   Ⓓ decided

© SSI • DO NOT DUPLICATE

8. Summer classes were in **abeyance** while the school's boiler was brought up to code.

Ⓐ disrepair

Ⓑ use

Ⓒ suspension

Ⓓ uncertainty

9. The city of Jerusalem is **sacrosanct** to Christians, Muslims, and Jews.

Ⓐ exotic

Ⓑ common

Ⓒ secular

Ⓓ sacred

10. A **tenet** of the practice of medicine is to do no harm.

Ⓐ rule

Ⓑ option

Ⓒ lie

Ⓓ suggestion

Choose the best way to complete each sentence or answer each question. Then fill in the circle next to your answer.

11. When she was offered a salary "**commensurate** with her experience," how did Sara expect to be paid?

Ⓐ at a higher rate than her last job

Ⓑ at a lower rate than she deserved

Ⓒ without regard to her experience

Ⓓ proportionately with her experience

12. Which way is a building's **facade** most likely to face?

Ⓐ toward the street

Ⓑ toward the pool

Ⓒ toward the setting sun

Ⓓ toward the neighboring building

13. Which of the following best describes a **gargoyle?**

Ⓐ charming

Ⓑ grotesque

Ⓒ functional

Ⓓ warm

14. When Aunt Iva reflected on the **pinnacle** of her career, she was thinking about its

Ⓐ beginning.

Ⓑ low point.

Ⓒ high point.

Ⓓ end.

15. Upon what does something **sensuous** act?

Ⓐ a stage

Ⓑ the intellect

Ⓒ the senses

Ⓓ a weakness

© SSI • DO NOT DUPLICATE

Standardized Test Preview/Practice

1. The flying buttress, developed in the twelfth century, provided — to bigger, heavier castles and cathedrals.

   (A) protection
   (B) moats
   (C) bricks
   (D) support
   (E) foundations

2. The musician dealt with his — by composing a requiem for his father.

   (A) grief
   (B) joy
   (C) surprise
   (D) gratitude
   (E) guilt

3. SENSUOUS : AGREEABLE ::

   (A) strident : unpleasant
   (B) beautiful : aesthetic
   (C) loud : rhythmic
   (D) delicious : repulsive
   (E) putrid : toxic

4. Supporters of both parties were thrilled when the candidates transcended their — with a good-natured exhibition for the —.

   (A) votes . . polls
   (B) schedules . . publicity
   (C) preferences . . quarrel
   (D) boundaries . . campaign
   (E) differences . . fundraiser

5. The police taped off the venue where the body was discovered so that the curious would not disturb the —.

   (A) victim
   (B) witnesses
   (C) investigators
   (D) crime scene
   (E) deceased

© SSI • DO NOT DUPLICATE

Name _____ Date _____

Lesson 15 Test

Find a SYNONYM for each bold word. Then fill in the circle next to your answer.

1. Pam enjoyed her office role as the **arbiter** of grammatical correctness.

   Ⓐ advocate
   Ⓑ expert
   Ⓒ judge
   Ⓓ guardian

2. Less-experienced coworkers were intimidated by the **coterie** of the company's top salespeople.

   Ⓐ clique
   Ⓑ confidence
   Ⓒ success
   Ⓓ talent

3. The **graphic** violence in the film made Elena queasy.

   Ⓐ understated
   Ⓑ terrible
   Ⓒ vivid
   Ⓓ implied

4. Lars considered it an **inimical** act when David drove across the flowerbeds that lined the driveway.

   Ⓐ aggressive
   Ⓑ accidental
   Ⓒ clumsy
   Ⓓ hostile

5. With the **inordinate** demands work and school were putting on her time lately, Cassie was beginning to miss her friends.

   Ⓐ unpredictable
   Ⓑ constant
   Ⓒ excessive
   Ⓓ frequent

Find an ANTONYM for each bold word. Then fill in the circle next to your answer.

6. Scientists believe there is a correlation between recent increases in average annual temperatures and the **concomitant** shrinkage of the polar ice caps.

   Ⓐ unrelated
   Ⓑ accompanying
   Ⓒ coincidental
   Ⓓ exaggerated

7. When it came time to vote on the proposal, Richard **demurred,** saying he preferred to wait until all the facts were in.

   Ⓐ acquiesced
   Ⓑ withdrew
   Ⓒ abstained
   Ⓓ disagreed

© SSI • DO NOT DUPLICATE

8. Wearing a seatbelt has been shown to drastically reduce the **inimical** effects of traffic accidents.

   Ⓐ harmful
   Ⓑ beneficial
   Ⓒ costly
   Ⓓ psychological

9. Ally found Jim's intention to cheat on the midterm **repugnant.**

   Ⓐ harmless
   Ⓑ distasteful
   Ⓒ offensive
   Ⓓ agreeable

10. Accustomed to eating in front of the television, Julie was afraid she would embarrass herself at a function as **genteel** as an afternoon tea.

   Ⓐ amusing
   Ⓑ pretentious
   Ⓒ stuffy
   Ⓓ vulgar

Choose the best way to complete each sentence or answer each question. Then fill in the circle next to your answer.

11. To prepare for Jorge's surprise party, a **conclave** of friends and family

   Ⓐ spoke often.
   Ⓑ discussed it casually.
   Ⓒ met secretly.
   Ⓓ spread the news.

12. An **enticing** invitation is least likely to do which of the following?

   Ⓐ intrigue
   Ⓑ allure
   Ⓒ persuade
   Ⓓ repulse

13. Someone with **genteel** manners is most likely to be described as

   Ⓐ polite.
   Ⓑ crass.
   Ⓒ arrogant.
   Ⓓ snobbish.

14. Which of the following best describes an **oligarchy?**

   Ⓐ a commune
   Ⓑ a democracy
   Ⓒ a business
   Ⓓ a government

15. Derrick **flaunted** his perfect score, rather than sparing his classmates' egos by being less

   Ⓐ shy.
   Ⓑ conspicuous.
   Ⓒ cruel.
   Ⓓ rude.

© SSI • DO NOT DUPLICATE

Standardized Test Preview/Practice

1. GRAPHIC : EYE ::

   Ⓐ oral : teeth

   Ⓑ musical : ear

   Ⓒ aromatic : smell

   Ⓓ delicious : taste

   Ⓔ sharp : nerve

2. Although Mr. Matsumoto hated to do anything — , he was enticed to perform the ludicrous "sock dance" to — his sick granddaughter.

   Ⓐ serious . . frighten

   Ⓑ physical . . heal

   Ⓒ showy . . embarrass

   Ⓓ childish . . bore

   Ⓔ undignified . . amuse

3. REDOUBTABLE : FEAR ::

   Ⓐ pleasant : face

   Ⓑ gratuitous : doubt

   Ⓒ intimidating : grimace

   Ⓓ tranquilizing : calm

   Ⓔ comforting : tension

4. The bakery was asking such inordinate — for simple cupcakes, we decided to shop around for a better deal.

   Ⓐ notice

   Ⓑ quantities

   Ⓒ lead time

   Ⓓ credit

   Ⓔ prices

5. Despite his doctor's repeated warnings that fast food was inimical to both his heart and his waistline, Lawrence — break his french fry habit.

   Ⓐ vowed to

   Ⓑ could not

   Ⓒ tried to

   Ⓓ agreed to

   Ⓔ should not

© SSI • DO NOT DUPLICATE

Lesson 16 > Test

Find a SYNONYM for each bold word. Then fill in the circle next to your answer.

1. After taking his exams, Diego loaded all his **chattels** into his truck and headed home for summer vacation.

   Ⓐ responsibilities
   Ⓑ property
   Ⓒ friends
   Ⓓ cousins

2. The pep squad did their best to counteract the **listlessness** of the fans at the football game.

   Ⓐ apathy
   Ⓑ anger
   Ⓒ disgust
   Ⓓ energy

3. Eager to explore life beyond the pasturelands, Chuck applied to colleges at every **metropolis** in the country.

   Ⓐ hamlet
   Ⓑ city
   Ⓒ village
   Ⓓ suburb

4. We **sequestered** ourselves all weekend to meet the Monday deadline.

   Ⓐ punished
   Ⓑ admonished
   Ⓒ amused
   Ⓓ secluded

5. Hal tried to **subvert** the school dress code by printing and circulating his own version of the rules.

   Ⓐ ridicule
   Ⓑ endorse
   Ⓒ undermine
   Ⓓ overrule

Find an ANTONYM for each bold word. Then fill in the circle next to your answer.

6. A high fever left Moira so **listless** that she hardly left her bedroom for four days.

   Ⓐ indifferent
   Ⓑ weak
   Ⓒ spiritless
   Ⓓ enthusiastic

7. Since she was a generally tidy person, all Ellie's house needed was a **perfunctory** straightening to prepare for visitors.

   Ⓐ major
   Ⓑ quick
   Ⓒ thorough
   Ⓓ surface

© SSI • DO NOT DUPLICATE

8. Ward's father threatened to **sequester** the car all weekend if he delayed painting the living room any longer.

   Ⓐ bestow
   Ⓑ seize
   Ⓒ hide
   Ⓓ enjoy

9. Barbara and Taria stopped at the gas station, the grocery store, the florist, the bakery, and the card shop before arriving at the hospital, the **terminus** of their odyssey.

   Ⓐ periphery
   Ⓑ layover
   Ⓒ purpose
   Ⓓ beginning

10. Max was unprepared for the **virulent** criticism he received at his first writers' workshop meeting.

    Ⓐ endless
    Ⓑ benevolent
    Ⓒ constructive
    Ⓓ passionate

Choose the best way to complete each sentence or answer each question. Then fill in the circle next to your answer.

11. Which of the following is least related to **chattel?**

    Ⓐ furniture
    Ⓑ livestock
    Ⓒ real estate
    Ⓓ appliances

12. Which of the following is most likely to be described as **commodious?**

    Ⓐ a bathroom
    Ⓑ a ballroom
    Ⓒ a bedroom
    Ⓓ a broom closet

13. **Limbo** has the least to do with which of the following?

    Ⓐ attention
    Ⓑ neglect
    Ⓒ transition
    Ⓓ disregard

14. Which of the following is least likely to describe a **virulent** outbreak of food poisoning?

    Ⓐ deadly
    Ⓑ dangerous
    Ⓒ widespread
    Ⓓ harmless

15. A **metropolitan** city is most likely to be described as

    Ⓐ important.
    Ⓑ scary.
    Ⓒ polluted.
    Ⓓ crowded.

© SSI • DO NOT DUPLICATE

Standardized Test Preview/Practice

1. ARCHIVES : HISTORICAL ::

   Ⓐ library : literary

   Ⓑ headline : abbreviated

   Ⓒ media : newsworthy

   Ⓓ prophesy : dire

   Ⓔ superstition : luck

2. CONFLAGRATION : FIRE ::

   Ⓐ volcano : lava

   Ⓑ blizzard : rain

   Ⓒ drought : rain

   Ⓓ tornado : wind

   Ⓔ earthquake : aftershock

3. The Alveys were — when the contractors were able to — the ramshackle 1920s bungalow to the pristine condition they had envisioned.

   Ⓐ confused .. elevate

   Ⓑ suspicious .. rebuild

   Ⓒ thrilled .. restore

   Ⓓ appalled .. convert

   Ⓔ pleased .. patch

4. Although she was always outwardly —, Yvette liked to be subversive at work by hiding faxes intended for her officemates.

   Ⓐ unusual

   Ⓑ enthusiastic

   Ⓒ friendly

   Ⓓ hostile

   Ⓔ cooperative

5. Thanks to family records and visits to archives all over the Northeast and Midwest, Marty could trace his lineage back to his earliest — in the U.S.

   Ⓐ experience

   Ⓑ visits

   Ⓒ memories

   Ⓓ ancestor

   Ⓔ home

© SSI • DO NOT DUPLICATE

Lesson 17 Test

Find a SYNONYM for each bold word. Then fill in the circle next to your answer.

1. Josef Stalin, premier of the Soviet Union from 1941 until 1953, was a powerful **autocrat** who dealt harshly with anyone who opposed him.

   Ⓐ politician
   Ⓑ mockery
   Ⓒ lunatic
   Ⓓ tyrant

2. One **caustic** comment from Enrique was enough to make his sensitive siblings cry.

   Ⓐ challenging
   Ⓑ sarcastic
   Ⓒ silly
   Ⓓ inappropriate

3. Shannon admired her brother's **felicitous** manner in everything from casual cookouts to formal business meetings.

   Ⓐ appropriate
   Ⓑ awkward
   Ⓒ competent
   Ⓓ knowledgeable

4. Wilson was stunned to learn that Beth was so **mercenary** that she expected to be paid for her summer internship at the women's shelter.

   Ⓐ poor
   Ⓑ optimistic
   Ⓒ naive
   Ⓓ greedy

5. Eliza knew she could survive the layoff, since she had been raised by a **parsimonious** father who showed her how to stretch every dollar.

   Ⓐ indulgent
   Ⓑ frugal
   Ⓒ patient
   Ⓓ clever

Find an ANTONYM for each bold word. Then fill in the circle next to your answer.

6. Mobutu Sese Seko ruled Zaire as an **autocracy** from 1965 until 1997.

   Ⓐ dictatorship
   Ⓑ triumvirate
   Ⓒ democracy
   Ⓓ monarchy

7. Russ's illness had **debilitated** him so badly that he had to rest every few minutes.

   Ⓐ empowered
   Ⓑ embarrassed
   Ⓒ trapped
   Ⓓ prepared

© SSI • DO NOT DUPLICATE

8. Andrea believed that, more than money or status, the most important thing was to lead a **felicitous** life.

Ⓐ pleasant
Ⓑ diligent
Ⓒ unfortunate
Ⓓ carefree

9. Soldiering has always been a career, but rather than being paid to be loyal and ready, as in modern armies, **mercenaries** used to fight for whichever side was prepared to pay.

Ⓐ peasants
Ⓑ knights
Ⓒ officers
Ⓓ volunteers

10. Being the granddaughter of a Wild West train robber gave Annie a **notoriety** that she would have happily done without.

Ⓐ power
Ⓑ popularity
Ⓒ anonymity
Ⓓ reputation

Choose the best way to complete each sentence or answer each question. Then fill in the circle next to your answer.

11. Which of the following is most likely to be **caustic?**

Ⓐ oil
Ⓑ butter
Ⓒ aloe
Ⓓ bleach

12. Which of the following people most needs to be **forthright?**

Ⓐ a doctor
Ⓑ a salesperson
Ⓒ a librarian
Ⓓ an entertainer

13. Someone who is **impecunious** is most likely to lack what?

Ⓐ talent
Ⓑ manners
Ⓒ money
Ⓓ friends

14. Which of the following is least associated with having a **jaundiced** attitude?

Ⓐ jealousy
Ⓑ even-handedness
Ⓒ hostility
Ⓓ resentment

15. Karen had incurred thousands of dollars in credit card debt through foolishness, which she now intended to pay off through **parsimony.** What is Karen's lifestyle most likely to be?

Ⓐ joyless
Ⓑ whimsical
Ⓒ opulent
Ⓓ penurious

© SSI • DO NOT DUPLICATE

Standardized Test Preview/Practice

1. Nicolae Ceausescu, the autocratic — of communist Romania, was ousted by a public — in 1989 that ended in his execution.

   Ⓐ ruler . . uprising

   Ⓑ spokesperson . . investigation

   Ⓒ ambassador . . hearing

   Ⓓ scapegoat . . trial

   Ⓔ leader . . invitation

2. Mata Hari, World War I's most infamous —, was an emissary for France convicted of carrying out duplicitous missions on behalf of —.

   Ⓐ victim . . her kidnappers

   Ⓑ performer . . the audience

   Ⓒ icon . . her husband

   Ⓓ messenger . . the military

   Ⓔ spy . . the enemy

3. JAUNDICED : YELLOW ::

   Ⓐ enfeebled : small

   Ⓑ morose : blue

   Ⓒ ashen : gray

   Ⓓ inexperienced : clumsy

   Ⓔ angry : loud

4. Although he needed a job, Rob was still too — by his public ouster to risk that his former manager might — pejorative things to prospective employers who called for a reference.

   Ⓐ angry . . lead

   Ⓑ humbled . . show

   Ⓒ indignant . . do

   Ⓓ embarrassed . . say

   Ⓔ stunned . . throw

5. Kirsten wondered how her parents had been together for so long, when one subscribes to the precept "Waste not; want not," and the other — that "You can't take it with you."

   Ⓐ denies

   Ⓑ believes

   Ⓒ ensures

   Ⓓ suggests

   Ⓔ detests

© SSI • DO NOT DUPLICATE

Lesson 18 ▷ **Test**

Find a SYNONYM for each bold word. Then fill in the circle next to your answer.

1. His friends **derided** Eduardo for sacrificing his weekend to study for an exam that was still two weeks away.

   Ⓐ congratulated
   Ⓑ helped
   Ⓒ admired
   Ⓓ ridiculed

2. Uncle Tommy had the **effrontery** to suggest that the children should eat dinner on the back porch because they were wearing clothes he didn't like.

   Ⓐ cleverness
   Ⓑ audacity
   Ⓒ wisdom
   Ⓓ thoughtlessness

3. Afraid of being accused of **hypocrisy,** the author of the popular weight-loss book was careful to dispose of her cupcake wrappers several blocks away from her office.

   Ⓐ falseness
   Ⓑ sincerity
   Ⓒ dedication
   Ⓓ carelessness

4. The Gales braced for the **impending** tornado underground in the storm cellar.

   Ⓐ violent
   Ⓑ unpredictable
   Ⓒ routine
   Ⓓ imminent

5. Originality is one of several **criteria** judges use to determine which entry will win the grand prize at the science fair.

   Ⓐ precedent
   Ⓑ destruction
   Ⓒ gravity
   Ⓓ standards

Find an ANTONYM for each bold word. Then fill in the circle next to your answer.

6. Though it was supposed to be a political satire, local critics dismissed the experimental drama as being **bereft** of social conscience.

   Ⓐ trained
   Ⓑ stripped
   Ⓒ packed
   Ⓓ devoid

7. The detective needed to gather all the **pertinent** facts as he reconstructed the events on the night of the break-in.

   Ⓐ irrelevant
   Ⓑ interesting
   Ⓒ important
   Ⓓ illicit

© SSI • DO NOT DUPLICATE

8. Although the poisoning was an accident, Vicki feared **retribution** when the old oak trees on her street died.

Ⓐ reward
Ⓑ punishment
Ⓒ notoriety
Ⓓ recognition

9. Gandhi **espoused** nonviolent resistance to oppression, a philosophy later adopted by Martin Luther King Jr.

Ⓐ embraced
Ⓑ rejected
Ⓒ advocated
Ⓓ denied

10. Dormitory rules **proscribe** loud music after 10:00 P.M. on weeknights.

Ⓐ govern
Ⓑ tolerate
Ⓒ prohibit
Ⓓ encourage

Choose the best way to complete each sentence or answer each question. Then fill in the circle next to your answer.

11. When a suggestion meets with **derision,** how do people most likely feel about it?

Ⓐ intimidated
Ⓑ scornful
Ⓒ attracted
Ⓓ suspicious

12. Which of the following is most likely to be considered a **hypocrite?**

Ⓐ a doctor who smokes
Ⓑ a teacher who reads
Ⓒ a criminal who lies
Ⓓ a dentist who flosses

13. Once something is **promulgated,** it is least likely to be

Ⓐ accepted.
Ⓑ newsworthy.
Ⓒ understood.
Ⓓ secret.

14. The right to petition the government for **redress** of grievances means that Americans can ask their government to

Ⓐ repeat wrongs.
Ⓑ deny wrongs.
Ⓒ correct wrongs.
Ⓓ admit wrongs.

15. A **regime** is most closely related to which of the following?

Ⓐ a corporation
Ⓑ a military
Ⓒ a government
Ⓓ a charity

© SSI • DO NOT DUPLICATE

Standardized Test Preview/Practice

1. Neighbors — Marcia's espousal of a green — as hypocritical, because they knew she didn't recycle anything.

   Ⓐ mocked . . lifestyle

   Ⓑ admired . . philosophy

   Ⓒ misunderstood . . ideal

   Ⓓ embraced . . lawn

   Ⓔ condemned . . tenet

2. INCENSED : ANGRY ::

   Ⓐ flattered : proud

   Ⓑ mortified : embarrassed

   Ⓒ apathetic : tired

   Ⓓ disconsolate : joyful

   Ⓔ elongated : molded

3. The — of the investment scheme had to substantiate their — before they could apply for redress.

   Ⓐ victims . . losses

   Ⓑ managers . . profits

   Ⓒ investigators . . evidence

   Ⓓ masterminds . . gains

   Ⓔ discoverers . . proof

4. BEREFT : GRIEVE ::

   Ⓐ surprised : forfeit

   Ⓑ wealthy : donate

   Ⓒ talented : perform

   Ⓓ elated : rejoice

   Ⓔ fortuitous : gamble

5. The expression "to read someone the riot act" comes from an eighteenth-century law that a specific — had to be promulgated to a dangerous mob before authorities could force people to disperse.

   Ⓐ announcement

   Ⓑ punishment

   Ⓒ weapon

   Ⓓ right

   Ⓔ question

© SSI • DO NOT DUPLICATE

Lesson 19 Test

Find a SYNONYM for each bold word. Then fill in the circle next to your answer.

1. Many Italian artists worked under the **aegis** of the powerful Borgia family.

   Ⓐ attention
   Ⓑ sponsorship
   Ⓒ ire
   Ⓓ fear

2. Even though their value was entirely sentimental, Aunt Mildred cherished the **baubles** she had collected from her admirers through the years.

   Ⓐ forks
   Ⓑ trinkets
   Ⓒ letters
   Ⓓ proposals

3. My grandmother was very superstitious and considered even the most common daily occurrences to be **portentous.**

   Ⓐ ominous
   Ⓑ insignificant
   Ⓒ interesting
   Ⓓ entertaining

4. Because of his children's illness, Mr. Tate gave us a **reprieve** on our deadline.

   Ⓐ escape
   Ⓑ respite
   Ⓒ option
   Ⓓ hint

5. Lewis and Clark's mission was to find a **viable** route to the Pacific Ocean.

   Ⓐ actual
   Ⓑ safe
   Ⓒ workable
   Ⓓ convoluted

Find an ANTONYM for each bold word. Then fill in the circle next to your answer.

6. Trey's approval of forming a neighborhood watch was **consolidated** when his garden statuary was vandalized.

   Ⓐ disregarded
   Ⓑ reversed
   Ⓒ destroyed
   Ⓓ strengthened

7. Leigh decided to **consolidate** the contents of many small bags into one main bag.

   Ⓐ unite
   Ⓑ combine
   Ⓒ separate
   Ⓓ remove

© SSI • DO NOT DUPLICATE

8. While studying for her pre-med finals, LaTasha had an **epiphany** that her true calling was the law.

   Ⓐ fear
   Ⓑ awareness
   Ⓒ message
   Ⓓ suspicion

9. The nominee was gifted with so **stentorian** a voice that she could captivate large groups without the need for amplification.

   Ⓐ monotonous
   Ⓑ commanding
   Ⓒ charismatic
   Ⓓ quiet

10. Erika preferred to wear **pendulous** jewelry because she felt that it was particularly dramatic.

   Ⓐ immobile
   Ⓑ expensive
   Ⓒ understated
   Ⓓ flowing

Choose the best way to complete each sentence or answer each question. Then fill in the circle next to your answer.

11. Which of the following best describes an **epiphany?**

   Ⓐ evolutionary
   Ⓑ vague
   Ⓒ gradual
   Ⓓ sudden

12. A **portent** is most related to things in the

   Ⓐ pantry.
   Ⓑ library.
   Ⓒ future.
   Ⓓ subconscious.

13. Which of the following is most related to **tenure?**

   Ⓐ pay rate
   Ⓑ time period
   Ⓒ authority
   Ⓓ hobbies

14. Which of the following professions most needs to be **pragmatic?**

   Ⓐ poet
   Ⓑ philosopher
   Ⓒ general
   Ⓓ historian

15. Which of the following is least likely to describe a **reprieve** from a responsibility?

   Ⓐ inconvenient
   Ⓑ temporary
   Ⓒ welcome
   Ⓓ relief

© SSI • DO NOT DUPLICATE

Standardized Test Preview/Practice

1. Although a few were — that their paychecks might be reduced, most — were complaisant regarding the summer moratorium on working overtime.

   Ⓐ thrilled . . vacationers
   Ⓑ sad . . students
   Ⓒ certain . . customers
   Ⓓ disappointed . . employees
   Ⓔ afraid . . renters

2. Rather than — the rabbits' depredation of the vegetable garden, each new deterrent seemed only to consolidate their —.

   Ⓐ stopping . . determination
   Ⓑ encouraging . . fear
   Ⓒ admitting . . enjoyment
   Ⓓ retarding . . regret
   Ⓔ admiring . . hunger

3. PENDULOUS : HAMMOCK ::

   Ⓐ loose : lid
   Ⓑ malleable : tin
   Ⓒ gaudy : attire
   Ⓓ forthright : companion
   Ⓔ munificent : miser

4. Convinced their intentions were — even if their approach was —, Principal Moxley unilaterally reprieved the Robin Hood gang.

   Ⓐ harmless . . insane
   Ⓑ charitable . . criminal
   Ⓒ inspired . . selfish
   Ⓓ selfish . . inventive
   Ⓔ malicious . . misguided

5. Despite Nancy's assurance that a rubber tree was viable in Maine, my plant — within weeks of our arrival.

   Ⓐ bloomed
   Ⓑ died
   Ⓒ flourished
   Ⓓ disappeared
   Ⓔ pollinated

© SSI • DO NOT DUPLICATE

Lesson 20 Test

Find a SYNONYM for each bold word. Then fill in the circle next to your answer.

1. Robert rushed home from school, knowing his mother would **excoriate** him if his room was still a mess by the time she got home from work.

   Ⓐ forgive
   Ⓑ punish
   Ⓒ berate
   Ⓓ deride

2. One of Anna's **idiosyncratic** habits was that she always served dessert first.

   Ⓐ quirky
   Ⓑ unfortunate
   Ⓒ grisly
   Ⓓ flawed

3. Ms. Morse's **pedagogical** talents were such that she could make calculus accessible to even the most confused.

   Ⓐ mathematical
   Ⓑ intimidating
   Ⓒ teaching
   Ⓓ illustrative

4. Even after watching the debate, Greg did not develop a **stance** on capital punishment.

   Ⓐ justification
   Ⓑ opinion
   Ⓒ grip
   Ⓓ objection

5. Though she wanted to continue studying, Dawn feared the **deleterious** effects of staying up all night on her ability to concentrate during the exam.

   Ⓐ intellectual
   Ⓑ creative
   Ⓒ somnolent
   Ⓓ harmful

Find an ANTONYM for each bold word. Then fill in the circle next to your answer.

6. His uncle's **grisly** war stories gave Patrick nightmares.

   Ⓐ typical
   Ⓑ unbelievable
   Ⓒ horrible
   Ⓓ pleasant

7. Thanksgiving at the McKinleys' house was a daylong parade of family **idiosyncrasies.**

   Ⓐ recipes
   Ⓑ stories
   Ⓒ habits
   Ⓓ normalities

© SSI • DO NOT DUPLICATE

8. The pharmacist warned Alex that the antibiotics could **negate** the effectiveness of other medicine he might be taking.

Ⓐ enhance

Ⓑ reduce

Ⓒ obstruct

Ⓓ affect

9. Ginnie continued to send handwritten thank-you notes, even though her friends assured her that e-mail had made them **passé.**

Ⓐ unnecessary

Ⓑ fashionable

Ⓒ pretentious

Ⓓ outmoded

10. Sam hid his **antipathy** to parsnips so as not to offend his hostess.

Ⓐ disgust

Ⓑ allergy

Ⓒ fondness

Ⓓ aversion

Choose the best way to complete each sentence or answer each question. Then fill in the circle next to your answer.

11. **Ambidextrous** writers can write with

Ⓐ their mouth.

Ⓑ their left hand.

Ⓒ either hand.

Ⓓ their feet.

12. Which of the following is most likely to be a **pedagogue?**

Ⓐ a dairy farmer

Ⓑ a scoutmaster

Ⓒ a shopkeeper

Ⓓ a pastry chef

13. A **preponderance** is least related to

Ⓐ the majority.

Ⓑ superiority.

Ⓒ importance.

Ⓓ surprises.

14. A **stance** is most closely related to which of the following?

Ⓐ feet

Ⓑ arms

Ⓒ head

Ⓓ eyes

15. A **grisly** scene is least likely to be described as

Ⓐ grim.

Ⓑ ghastly.

Ⓒ attractive.

Ⓓ harsh.

© SSI • DO NOT DUPLICATE

Standardized Test Preview/Practice

1. EXTRAPOLATE : INFER ::

   Ⓐ adjudicate : settle
   Ⓑ estimate : count
   Ⓒ know : confuse
   Ⓓ suspect : wonder
   Ⓔ populate : shrink

2. Because of her maladroit — about needing to stop at the restaurant, the group imputed Katie with — Dan's surprise.

   Ⓐ pretext . . ensuring
   Ⓑ joke . . coordinating
   Ⓒ charade . . preserving
   Ⓓ story . . ruining
   Ⓔ excuse . . perfecting

3. NEGATE : TRUTH ::

   Ⓐ deny : alibi
   Ⓑ marginalize : importance
   Ⓒ support : indulge
   Ⓓ admit : explanation
   Ⓔ announce : news

4. Based on the preponderance of —, the district attorney propounded a — of the crime.

   Ⓐ evidence . . theory
   Ⓑ attention . . timeline
   Ⓒ suspects . . explanation
   Ⓓ jurors . . prosecution
   Ⓔ weapons . . defense

5. Frank wished his sister would occasionally keep a — to herself, rather than excoriating him constantly.

   Ⓐ disappointment
   Ⓑ chore
   Ⓒ lesson
   Ⓓ viewpoint
   Ⓔ criticism

© SSI • DO NOT DUPLICATE

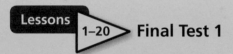

Read the passage. Choose the best answer for each sentence or question about a bold word. Then fill in the circle next to your answer.

What's in a Name?

Who wrote your favorite book? Are you sure? There is a good chance that the real writer of your favorite book has a name you do not recognize. There are myriad reasons for writers to want to mask their identities, and when they opt to do so, the first thing they reach for is a pen name. Adopting a pen name, also called a pseudonym or a *nom de plume,* is a perfectly legal and widely accepted practice in publishing. Authors' **duplicity** when they **purport** to be someone other than their true selves is considered minor. Pseudonyms are probably as old as the printed word. The reasons to **fabricate** one may be personal or professional, practical or utterly unfathomable. An **altruistic** author with a shocking true story to tell may choose a pseudonym in order to spare his or her family any embarrassment at being associated with the name.

One common reason authors have for using a pseudonym is that they fear they lack the professional credibility for their work to be taken seriously. By disguising the work's true source, the writers hope to **entice** a publisher to accept it on its own merit. In the early 1700s, a teenaged Ben Franklin, a printer's apprentice with practically no formal education, began submitting essays to his brother's newspaper under the name "Silence Dogood." The popular features would never have been published had the editor known his own little brother was responsible for writing them. Historically, many women writers published under male names either because it was considered improper for ladies to write novels or because some people thought it inconceivable that they could. Some notable female writers who used pseudonyms to **transcend** gender **disparities** in publishing were George Eliot (Mary Ann Evans) and Currer, Ellis, and Acton Bell (Charlotte, Emily, and Anne Brontë).

Another reason writers have assumed pen names is so that their success in one field or genre would not interfere with their credibility in another. The author of the children's fantasy classic *Alice's Adventures in Wonderland* wrote fiction under the name Lewis Carroll because as Charles Lutwidge Dodgson, he held **tenure** at England's Oxford University and published books on mathematics. Mystery master Agatha Christie wrote romantic novels as Mary Westmacott, so as not to disappoint fans who picked up a love story expecting a thriller.

Another issue of credibility that may be solved by a pen name is not in the writer's credentials but in the name itself. Writers often choose a name that reflects the subject matter of their story. That way, audiences will feel that the author has a **propensity** for writing particular subject matter. Writers who focus on historical fiction set in a particular locale may be more believable if their names support the idea that they should have particular knowledge about that place. For example, a writer of Westerns might feel the name Tex Masterson has more "authenticity" on the cover of a book than a name like Cyril Higginbotham.

© SSI • DO NOT DUPLICATE

The desire to protect their own privacy may also be responsible for some people's choosing pseudonyms. Authors who **espouse** controversial ideas or reveal family secrets may choose a pseudonym to avoid publicity or **antipathy** from the audience. While most writers dream of becoming famous, some wish to avoid the **thrall** of celebrity. Some practical business considerations may also make the use of a pen name necessary. Using a pen name may allow writers to continue working on other projects if a contract prohibits them from publishing under a certain name. For others, hiding their true identity is mandated by the terms of the publishing contract; some publishers require their authors to use a pen name.

Then there are those pen names that are well known to most people, but for which the reason for adoption remains a mystery. Classic American **raconteur** Mark Twain was born Samuel Clemens. He adopted the pseudonym as a young journalist in Nevada because it reminded him of his favorite times traveling on the Mississippi River by riverboat. The boat's leadsmen would periodically check distance between the bottom of the steamboat and the riverbed, and when the depth was the dangerously shallow twelve feet, he would sound the alert by shouting, "By the mark, twain!" It may be that Samuel Clemens needed an alter ego more than a pen name.

Our enjoyment of a work is often closely tied to what we believe to be the source of that work. Writers and publishers understand this. They try to manipulate our impressions accordingly. A book's writer may be as fictional as the book itself, but how much does that matter if you enjoy the read? Remember the adage, "You can't judge a book by its cover"? Perhaps we should add, "You can't judge a book by its author."

1. As used in the second paragraph, to **entice** means to do what?

   Ⓐ placate

   Ⓑ extort

   Ⓒ persuade

   Ⓓ deceive

2. As used in this passage, an ANTONYM for **espouse** is

   Ⓐ support.

   Ⓑ preserve.

   Ⓒ discuss.

   Ⓓ oppose.

3. As used in the fifth paragraph, a SYNONYM for **antipathy** is

   Ⓐ aversion.

   Ⓑ tolerance.

   Ⓒ stalking.

   Ⓓ invasion.

© SSI • DO NOT DUPLICATE

4. As used in the second paragraph, **disparities** is most closely related to

Ⓐ prejudices.

Ⓑ preferences.

Ⓒ differences.

Ⓓ aptitudes.

5. As used in this passage, **propensity** is most closely related to what type of tendency?

Ⓐ natural

Ⓑ practiced

Ⓒ knowledgeable

Ⓓ learned

6. As used in the first paragraph, an ANTONYM for **fabricate** is

Ⓐ invent.

Ⓑ reveal.

Ⓒ destroy.

Ⓓ deny.

7. As used in the third paragraph, **tenure** is most closely related to

Ⓐ position.

Ⓑ prestige.

Ⓒ power.

Ⓓ pay.

8. Which is a SYNONYM for **altruistic?**

Ⓐ greedy

Ⓑ selfish

Ⓒ selfless

Ⓓ harmless

9. Which of the following is NOT a SYNONYM for **transcend?**

Ⓐ exceed

Ⓑ fight

Ⓒ surpass

Ⓓ rise above

10. As used in the first paragraph, **duplicity** refers to all of the following except

Ⓐ deceit.

Ⓑ publicity.

Ⓒ secrecy.

Ⓓ dishonesty.

© SSI • DO NOT DUPLICATE

Standardized Test Preview/Practice

1. In the first paragraph, **purport** is least related to

   Ⓐ claim.

   Ⓑ imply.

   Ⓒ assert.

   Ⓓ deny.

   Ⓔ profess.

2. As used in the sixth paragraph, **raconteur** is most closely related to

   Ⓐ songs.

   Ⓑ stories.

   Ⓒ lectures.

   Ⓓ trends.

   Ⓔ demoted.

3. As used in paragraph five, **thrall** is a state of

   Ⓐ powerlessness.

   Ⓑ confusion.

   Ⓒ bliss.

   Ⓓ publicity.

   Ⓔ control.

4. Which of the following is most likely to **espouse** something?

   Ⓐ an accountant

   Ⓑ a student

   Ⓒ an advocate

   Ⓓ a police officer

   Ⓔ an actor

5. Which of the following is most likely to engage in **duplicity?**

   Ⓐ a judge

   Ⓑ a minister

   Ⓒ a student

   Ⓓ a con artist

   Ⓔ a merchant

© SSI • DO NOT DUPLICATE

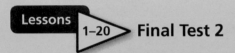

Final Test 2

Read the passage. Choose the best answer for each sentence or question about a bold word. Then fill in the circle next to your answer.

Name That Hurricane

A hurricane belongs to the **triumvirate** of storms that also includes tropical cyclones and typhoons. Hurricanes are known to exist only in the Atlantic Ocean, typhoons are found in the Pacific Ocean, and tropical cyclones are found in the Indian Ocean. A hurricane begins as a weak storm system that forms over warm, tropical waters. As the strength of the winds increases, the storm is first called a tropical depression, then a tropical storm, then a hurricane. It takes days for a full-force hurricane to develop from its **incipient** stage, if it develops at all. Unlike earthquakes or tornadoes, hurricanes give people in the path of the storm time to protect themselves.

The severe winds of a hurricane revolve around a central "eye," a relatively **listless** area. Around this "eye" area, storm clouds move in a counter-clockwise motion as they cause the sea below to **undulate** wildly. The word *hurricane* is thought to be from the West Indian word meaning "big wind." Others believe the **etymology** is related to the Indian word *huracan* (evil spirit) or from the Mayan word *huraken* (bad weather).

Beginning in 1873, the Army Signal Corps attempted to issue storm warnings, although there was no **viable** tracking system in the U.S. until 1890. The practice of naming hurricanes began to help identify storms and track them as they move across the ocean. Military weather forecasters began giving women's names to significant storms during World War II after George R. Stewart used a woman's name for a storm in his 1941 novel, *Storm*. Then in 1950, the World Meteorological Organization (WMO) agreed to an alphabetical system, using a code created by the military. The first Atlantic hurricane named according to this system was Able, in 1950. After careful consideration, officials soon realized the naming procedure would be less **utilitarian** if more than one powerful hurricane met the **criteria** in the same order in a season. So, in 1953 the organization adopted a rotating series of women's names. Names of **notorious** storms were retired.

The practice of exclusively using female names ended to **appease** groups that objected to these forces of destruction always being thought of as women. In 1978, male and female names were used to name storms in the eastern Pacific. A year later, an alternating male/female naming process was included in lists for the Atlantic and the Gulf of Mexico. The name lists include international names because hurricanes affect many nations and are tracked by the weather services of many countries. Twenty-one names are reserved each year and the names are recycled every six years. When a name is retired, the WMO chooses a new name to replace it. The letters Q, U, X, Y, and Z are not included because of the scarcity of names beginning with those letters.

Hurricanes are categorized according to the strength of their winds, using the Saffir-Simpson Hurricane Scale. A Category 1 storm has the lowest wind speeds, while a Category 5 hurricane has the most **frenetic.** The Tropical Prediction Center near Miami, Florida, keeps a

© SSI • DO NOT DUPLICATE

constant watch on oceanic storm-breeding grounds. Hurricane season officially runs from the beginning of June to the end of November. Once a system with counter-clockwise rotation and wind speeds of 39 miles per hour or greater is detected, the Center considers it a tropical storm and gives it a name from the list for the current year. If its winds reach sustained speeds of 74 miles per hour, it then becomes classified as a hurricane.

Hurricanes usually affect the areas of the North Atlantic, the Caribbean **archipelago,** the Gulf of Mexico, and the Eastern Pacific. Hurricane Andrew, which hit the U.S. in 1992, produced an estimated $26 billion in damage and left 180,000 homeless in Florida. Prediction models now **portend** that, after Miami and New Orleans, New York City is the third most likely location for a hurricane catastrophe in a **metropolitan** area. If it happens, residents' safety will depend on the information we now know about hurricanes.

1. As used in the second paragraph, **etymology** is a SYNONYM for

   Ⓐ science.
   Ⓑ history.
   Ⓒ definition.
   Ⓓ pronunciation.

2. As used in the second paragraph, **undulate** is most closely related to

   Ⓐ waves.
   Ⓑ temperature.
   Ⓒ rotation.
   Ⓓ surface.

3. As used in the third paragraph, a SYNONYM for **viable** is

   Ⓐ popular.
   Ⓑ workable.
   Ⓒ acceptable.
   Ⓓ reliable.

4. To say a storm is **notorious** means that it is

   Ⓐ named for the cities it damaged.
   Ⓑ particularly powerful.
   Ⓒ common to all areas.
   Ⓓ remembered for the damage it caused.

5. As used in the fourth paragraph, **appease** most closely means

   Ⓐ taunt.
   Ⓑ pacify.
   Ⓒ honor.
   Ⓓ submit.

© SSI • DO NOT DUPLICATE

6. An ANTONYM for **frenetic,** as used in paragraph five, is

Ⓐ calm.

Ⓑ excited.

Ⓒ happy.

Ⓓ frenzied.

7. As used in the third paragraph, a SYNONYM for **utilitarian** is

Ⓐ practical.

Ⓑ useful.

Ⓒ beautiful.

Ⓓ confusing.

8. As used in the sixth paragraph, **portend** most nearly means

Ⓐ indicate.

Ⓑ guess.

Ⓒ threaten.

Ⓓ doubt.

9. The word **archipelago** refers to

Ⓐ islands.

Ⓑ regions.

Ⓒ nations.

Ⓓ continents.

10. Which of the following most applies to a city described as **metropolitan?**

Ⓐ big

Ⓑ crowded

Ⓒ important

Ⓓ imposing

© SSI • DO NOT DUPLICATE

Standardized Test Preview/Practice

1. In the second paragraph, **listless** implies a lack of

   Ⓐ restraint.

   Ⓑ rain.

   Ⓒ fury.

   Ⓓ energy.

   Ⓔ danger.

2. To **portend** is most closely related to what type of events?

   Ⓐ future

   Ⓑ current

   Ⓒ desirable

   Ⓓ unlikely

   Ⓔ historical

3. What best captures the meaning of the word **incipient** in the first paragraph?

   Ⓐ insignificant

   Ⓑ dangerous

   Ⓒ final

   Ⓓ harmless

   Ⓔ beginning

4. In the third paragraph, **criteria** most nearly means

   Ⓐ standards.

   Ⓑ reasons.

   Ⓒ levels.

   Ⓓ speed.

   Ⓔ notoriety.

5. A **triumvirate** relates to what?

   Ⓐ rotation

   Ⓑ number

   Ⓒ strength

   Ⓓ size

   Ⓔ family

© SSI • DO NOT DUPLICATE

Name _____ Date _____

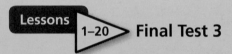

Read the passage. Choose the best answer for each sentence or question about a bold word. Then fill in the circle next to your answer.

A Friend in Need

The **genesis** of the Saint Bernard dog breed is inextricably bound to the mountain pass and the monastery that bear the same name. In the sixteenth century, the Saint Bernard Pass provided a route between Switzerland and Italy through the Alps. In 57 B.C.E. Julius Caesar attempted to secure safe passage over the Alps, but it was not until 7 or 6 B.C.E. that the Roman legions conquered the Alpine region and secured the pass. What would come to be known as the Saint Bernard Pass provided the most **expedient** route to the newly conquered province, Britannia. Later, the small path was improved to accommodate travelers and their carriages crossing the Alps.

The pass fell out of use for several hundred years before the monastery was built. It regained importance in medieval times, but was plagued by **marauders** who preyed on those using the pass. The Saint Bernard monastery was established in the pass about a millennium after the Romans first used it. Legend **postulates** that the Holy Saint Bernard of Montjou banished evil spirits and founded the monastery around 950. However, historical records of a meeting Saint Bernard had in 1086 renders that story unlikely. Experts believe that the monastery was actually founded around the year 1050. It included a hospice where travelers would receive three days' free meals and lodging.

Traders traveling through the pass brought dogs to the monastery until the 1100s. Then the route was largely unused for several hundred years, and no new dogs entered the Saint Bernard Monastery. It was during this time that the Saint Bernard breed arose. Records from 1700 note the first mountain guides assigned to accompany travelers to the other side of the pass. The Saint Bernard's **metier** was to accompany guides, as the dogs' excellent sense of direction proved most beneficial. Their broad chests were well suited to help clear paths for travelers, and the dogs also possessed an uncanny ability to maneuver through heavy fog and snowstorms, which have a **deleterious** effect on safe travel.

During the 200 years that the dogs served on the Saint Bernard Pass, approximately 2,000 **itinerants** were rescued. The dogs' sense of direction, compassion for humans, and adaptations to the harsh weather combined in a **proclivity** for rescue that saw hundreds of thousands of travelers safely through the **travails** of the pass. The last documented rescue dates from 1897, when a twelve-year-old boy was found nearly frozen and was awakened by a dog. The feature most often associated with the Saint Bernard, along with the oversized build and red-and-white coloring, is the barrel strapped beneath the dog's neck. The barrel, however, appears to be nothing more than a **fabrication** of some imaginative author.

The Saint Bernard was established as a pure breed with standards by Heinrich Schumacher in Switzerland in the 1850s. Many of today's Saint Bernards can trace their **lineage** to the dogs bred by Schumacher. Saint Bernards have plenty to offer aside from their

© SSI • DO NOT DUPLICATE

skill as lifesavers. The monks seem to think—and families in cooler climates around the world have come to agree—that the faithfulness, gentleness, and intelligence of this **redoubtable** breed makes Saint Bernards welcome additions to any household.

1. As used in the first paragraph, **genesis** is least related to

Ⓐ legend.

Ⓑ beginning.

Ⓒ origin.

Ⓓ creation.

2. An ANTONYM for **expedient,** as used in the first paragraph, is

Ⓐ dangerous.

Ⓑ useful.

Ⓒ inconvenient.

Ⓓ practical.

3. As used in the second paragraph, **marauders** is most closely related to

Ⓐ combatants.

Ⓑ bullies.

Ⓒ vagabonds.

Ⓓ criminals.

4. To **postulate** most nearly means to

Ⓐ assume.

Ⓑ proclaim.

Ⓒ know.

Ⓓ doubt.

5. As used in paragraph three, **metier** is most closely related to

Ⓐ talent.

Ⓑ work.

Ⓒ reward.

Ⓓ instinct.

© SSI • DO NOT DUPLICATE

6. As used in the third paragraph, an ANTONYM for **deleterious** is

Ⓐ gradual.

Ⓑ blinding.

Ⓒ harmless.

Ⓓ dangerous.

7. As used in the fourth paragraph, **itinerants** are most closely related to

Ⓐ freezing.

Ⓑ fleeing.

Ⓒ begging.

Ⓓ traveling.

8. Which is a SYNONYM for **proclivity?**

Ⓐ inclination

Ⓑ passion

Ⓒ talent

Ⓓ duty

9. Which of the following does not describe **travails?**

Ⓐ difficult

Ⓑ enjoyable

Ⓒ arduous

Ⓓ burdensome

10. As used in the fourth paragraph, **fabrication** most nearly means

Ⓐ illustration.

Ⓑ description.

Ⓒ invention.

Ⓓ fantasy.

© SSI • DO NOT DUPLICATE

Standardized Test Preview/Practice

1. In the fifth paragraph, **lineage** is least related to

   (A) descent.

   (B) ancestry.

   (C) family.

   (D) parentage.

   (E) nobility.

2. As used in the fifth paragraph, **redoubtable** is most closely related to

   (A) energy.

   (B) fear.

   (C) trouble.

   (D) respect.

   (E) society.

3. Which of the following is most closely related to a person's **genesis?**

   (A) birthday

   (B) graduation

   (C) anniversary

   (D) retirement

   (E) death

4. Which of the following is most likely to be described as **deleterious?**

   (A) a thunderstorm

   (B) poison

   (C) the ocean

   (D) ice

   (E) a headache

5. Which of these is most likely to be an **itinerant?**

   (A) an office manager

   (B) a police officer

   (C) a traveling salesman

   (D) a local politician

   (E) a bakery owner

© SSI • DO NOT DUPLICATE

Name _____   Date _____

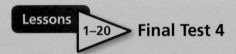
Read the passage. Choose the best answer for each sentence or question about a bold word. Then fill in the circle next to your answer.

Salt Shakes an Empire

Until the mid-twentieth century, India was a colony of the **behemoth** known as the British Empire. Mohandas "Mahatma" Gandhi, the father of India's independence from the empire, pioneered nonviolent civil disobedience, a tactic later used by the U.S. civil rights movement and by proponents of freedom everywhere. An important **tenet** of Gandhi's teaching was that protesters use nonviolence as a sign of strength. One of the famous Gandhi campaigns, the Salt March of 1930, was a nonviolent protest against the injustices of the British Government. This march attracted **disparate** participants from all levels of Indian society.

Salt was vital to the health and economy of India, and the British taxes on salt had an **inordinate** impact on the most impoverished sectors of Indian society. Not only did the salt laws force people out of commercial trade, but Indian citizens also had to pay a tax on the salt they needed for food preservation and cooking. Even **sacrosanct** cultural rituals involving salt were subject to taxation.

Taxed for years before the march, followers all over India began to disapprove of the government's practices. Gandhi decided the injustice should not be endured, and he found tremendous support for his cause. Before talk of protest, Gandhi tried to **reconcile** differences with the government by writing about his displeasure to Lord Irwin, viceroy of India. He wrote of the inequities of the tax as well of his intention to break the law.

Gandhi organized his march to the Arabian Sea in the spring of 1930. Gandhi and seventy-eight **zealous** followers left Gujarat for their 140-mile journey by foot to the ocean at Danda. The march drew people from large cities as well as from the **bucolic** Indian countryside. Local officials even resigned their posts to show their support. At the beginning of the march, Gandhi had only a few hundred followers. Almost 25 days later, the crowd had grown into the thousands. When they arrived at the western shore of India, Gandhi made his own salt from seawater in an act of civil disobedience.

Protestors in other parts of the country began similar opposition to the salt laws. As the protest grew along both coastlines, the British **flaunted** their power with violent attacks on activists. In Orissa, a meeting was organized to coincide with Gandhi's protest. As people scooped up handfuls of salt on the coast, police considered their actions **tantamount** to revolt and used clubs to knock the salt from protesters' hands. When force failed, thousands of *satyagrahis* (soldiers of civil disobedience) were arrested, but others continued. To suppress the strength of the movement, Gandhi was arrested on May 4, 1930, sleeping at a village near the sea. However, the incarceration of the movement's leader did not bring about the **abeyance** of defiance the British government had hoped for. Gandhi was released in 1931. After his release, he continued to work towards Indian independence, which was achieved in August 1947. He died a mere five months later.

© SSI • DO NOT DUPLICATE

The Salt March came to the world's attention due to Gandhi's **imperturbable** demeanor and ability to appeal to people across regional, class, and ethnic boundaries during his lifetime and beyond. Gandhi would have an enormous influence on Martin Luther King Jr. and other leaders who were motivated by his philosophy and his success through nonviolent civil disobedience.

1. As used in the first paragraph, **behemoth** is least related to

   Ⓐ antiquity.

   Ⓑ hugeness.

   Ⓒ vastness.

   Ⓓ power.

2. All of the following are SYNONYMS for **tenet** EXCEPT

   Ⓐ principle.

   Ⓑ belief.

   Ⓒ suggestion.

   Ⓓ truth.

3. As used in the first paragraph, an ANTONYM for **disparate** is

   Ⓐ impassioned.

   Ⓑ different.

   Ⓒ solemn.

   Ⓓ similar.

4. As used in the second paragraph, **inordinate** is most closely related to

   Ⓐ punitive.

   Ⓑ excess.

   Ⓒ lack.

   Ⓓ subtlety.

5. As used in this passage, **sacrosanct** most nearly means

   Ⓐ holy.

   Ⓑ culinary.

   Ⓒ casual.

   Ⓓ mundane.

© SSI • DO NOT DUPLICATE

6. As used in the third paragraph, to **reconcile** is most closely related to

Ⓐ discussing plans.

Ⓑ repairing communication.

Ⓒ achieving independence.

Ⓓ reaching agreement.

7. Which of the following is NOT a SYNONYM for **zealous?**

Ⓐ enthusiastic

Ⓑ insane

Ⓒ fervent

Ⓓ passionate

8. As used in paragraph four, **bucolic** most closely means

Ⓐ sophisticated.

Ⓑ rustic.

Ⓒ dusty.

Ⓓ lush.

9. Which of the following is NOT a SYNONYM for **flaunted,** as used in the fifth paragraph?

Ⓐ exhibited

Ⓑ displayed

Ⓒ paraded

Ⓓ disguised

10. As used in the fifth paragraph, an ANTONYM for **tantamount** is

Ⓐ opposite.

Ⓑ equivalent.

Ⓒ the same as.

Ⓓ comparable.

© SSI • DO NOT DUPLICATE

Standardized Test Preview/Practice

1. In the fifth paragraph, **abeyance** is most closely related to

   Ⓐ starting.
   Ⓑ interrupting.
   Ⓒ ending.
   Ⓓ stopping.
   Ⓔ continuing.

2. As used in the sixth paragraph, **imperturbable** is least related to being

   Ⓐ calm.
   Ⓑ composed.
   Ⓒ serene.
   Ⓓ emotional.
   Ⓔ stoic.

3. Which of the following is most likely to be described as a **behemoth?**

   Ⓐ a goldfish
   Ⓑ a shark
   Ⓒ a salmon
   Ⓓ a dolphin
   Ⓔ a whale

4. Which of the following is most likely to be considered **sacrosanct?**

   Ⓐ books
   Ⓑ pets
   Ⓒ vows
   Ⓓ fruit
   Ⓔ hobbies

5. Which of the following is most likely to be considered **zealous?**

   Ⓐ a dog catcher
   Ⓑ a campaign manager
   Ⓒ a pastry chef
   Ⓓ a fact checker
   Ⓔ a racecar driver

© SSI • DO NOT DUPLICATE

Answer Key

Lesson 1
1. C
2. A
3. B
4. C
5. C
6. B
7. D
8. A
9. B
10. D
11. B
12. B
13. C
14. D
15. A

STP/P
1. A
2. C
3. D
4. B
5. E

Lesson 2
1. C
2. B
3. D
4. A
5. B
6. B
7. A
8. B
9. C
10. B
11. C
12. B
13. D
14. A
15. D

STP/P
1. C
2. A
3. D
4. C
5. E

Lesson 3
1. A
2. C
3. D
4. A
5. D
6. B
7. B
8. C
9. C
10. A
11. C
12. D
13. A
14. B
15. B

STP/P
1. C
2. D
3. B
4. C
5. A

Lesson 4
1. D
2. C
3. B
4. D
5. A
6. B
7. C
8. B
9. B
10. C
11. B
12. A
13. C
14. C
15. B

STP/P
1. B
2. E
3. B
4. D
5. E

Lesson 5
1. C
2. A
3. C
4. B
5. B
6. C
7. A
8. C
9. D
10. D
11. C
12. D
13. A
14. D
15. C

STP/P
1. C
2. A
3. E
4. A
5. B

Lesson 6
1. D
2. C
3. C
4. A
5. A
6. B
7. C
8. A
9. D
10. A
11. C
12. C
13. D
14. D
15. C

STP/P
1. C
2. B
3. E
4. A
5. D

Lesson 7
1. B
2. A
3. B
4. D
5. A
6. D
7. A
8. B
9. B
10. C
11. C
12. D
13. A
14. B
15. A

STP/P
1. D
2. A
3. A
4. C
5. E

Lesson 8
1. D
2. A
3. B
4. C
5. A
6. D
7. C
8. A
9. D
10. A
11. A
12. D
13. C
14. B
15. A

STP/P
1. C
2. E
3. D
4. B
5. C

Lesson 9
1. B
2. A
3. C
4. B
5. C
6. A
7. B
8. D
9. C
10. B
11. A
12. B
13. A
14. D
15. B

STP/P
1. D
2. E
3. B
4. D
5. B

Lesson 10
1. A
2. C
3. A
4. B
5. C
6. D
7. B
8. D
9. B
10. A
11. B
12. D
13. B
14. A
15. D

STP/P
1. A
2. D
3. D
4. B
5. B

**Midterm Test 1
(Lessons 1–10)**
1. B
2. D
3. B
4. C
5. C
6. D
7. B
8. A
9. D
10. D

STP/P
1. A
2. D
3. A
4. C
5. B

**Midterm Test 2
(Lessons 1–10)**
1. D
2. C
3. B
4. D
5. C
6. D
7. B
8. A
9. D
10. C

STP/P
1. C
2. E
3. A
4. E
5. C

Lesson 11
1. A
2. D
3. A
4. D
5. B
6. C
7. B
8. C
9. A
10. D
11. C
12. C
13. A
14. B
15. C

STP/P
1. D
2. A
3. D
4. E
5. D

Answer Key

Lesson 12	Lesson 14	Lesson 16	Lesson 18	Lesson 20	Final Test 3
1. C	1. B	1. B	1. D	1. C	(Lessons 1–20)
2. A	2. D	2. A	2. B	2. A	1. A
3. D	3. A	3. B	3. A	3. C	2. C
4. A	4. A	4. D	4. D	4. B	3. D
5. B	5. D	5. C	5. D	5. D	4. A
6. A	6. B	6. D	6. C	6. D	5. B
7. D	7. D	7. C	7. A	7. D	6. C
8. B	8. B	8. A	8. A	8. A	7. D
9. A	9. C	9. D	9. B	9. B	8. A
10. B	10. C	10. B	10. D	10. C	9. B
11. D	11. D	11. C	11. B	11. C	10. C
12. C	12. A	12. B	12. A	12. B	
13. A	13. B	13. A	13. D	13. D	STP/P
14. B	14. C	14. D	14. C	14. A	1. E
15. C	15. C	15. A	15. C	15. C	2. D
					3. A
STP/P	STP/P	STP/P	STP/P	STP/P	4. B
1. D	1. D	1. A	1. A	1. A	5. C
2. B	2. A	2. D	2. B	2. D	
3. D	3. A	3. C	3. A	3. B	Final Test 4
4. B	4. E	4. E	4. D	4. A	(Lessons 1–20)
5. A	5. D	5. D	5. A	5. E	1. A
					2. C
Lesson 13	Lesson 15	Lesson 17	Lesson 19	Final Test 1	3. D
1. C	1. C	1. D	1. B	(Lessons 1–20)	4. B
2. A	2. A	2. B	2. B	1. C	5. A
3. D	3. C	3. A	3. A	2. D	6. D
4. B	4. D	4. D	4. B	3. A	7. B
5. A	5. C	5. B	5. C	4. C	8. B
6. A	6. A	6. C	6. C	5. A	9. D
7. D	7. A	7. A	7. C	6. C	10. A
8. B	8. B	8. C	8. D	7. A	
9. A	9. D	9. D	9. D	8. C	STP/P
10. B	10. D	10. C	10. A	9. B	1. B
11. C	11. C	11. D	11. D	10. B	2. D
12. A	12. D	12. A	12. C		3. E
13. C	13. A	13. C	13. B	STP/P	4. C
14. B	14. D	14. B	14. C	1. D	5. B
15. D	15. B	15. D	15. A	2. B	
				3. A	
STP/P	STP/P	STP/P	STP/P	4. C	
1. B	1. B	1. A	1. D	5. D	
2. D	2. E	2. E	2. A		
3. A	3. D	3. C	3. B	Final Test 2	
4. B	4. E	4. D	4. B	(Lessons 1–20)	
5. C	5. B	5. B	5. B	1. B	
				2. A	
				3. B	
				4. D	
				5. B	
				6. A	
				7. B	
				8. A	
				9. A	
				10. C	
				STP/P	
				1. D	
				2. A	
				3. E	
				4. A	
				5. B	